Hodder Gibson

Scottish Examination Materials

STANDARD GRADE
CHEMISTRY

Revision Notes & Questions

8/20/15

Norman Conquest

HODDER
GIBSON
PART OF HACHETTE LIVRE UK

Order queries: please contact Bookpoint Ltd, 130 Milton Park, Abingdon, Oxon OX14 4SB.
Telephone: (44) 01235 827720, Fax: (44) 01235 400454. Lines are open from 9.00–5.00,
Monday to Saturday, with a 24 hour message answering service. You can also order through
our website at www.hoddereducation.co.uk

British Library Cataloguing in Publication Data
A catalogue entry for this title is available from The British Library

ISBN-13: 978-0-340-69091-8

Published by Hodder Gibson, 2a Christie Street, Paisley PA1 1NB.
Tel: 0141 848 1609; Fax: 0141 889 6315; email: hoddergibson@hodder.co.uk
First published 1997
Impression number   12
Year   2008
Copyright ® 1997 Norman Conquest

Typeset by Transet Ltd, Coventry, England.
Printed in Great Britain for Hodder Gibson, 2a Christie Street, Paisley, PA1 1NB, Scotland, UK
by Martins The Printers, Berwick-upon-Tweed.

Contents

Introduction   iv

Part 1   Topic by Topic: Summaries and Questions   **1**

1   Introducing chemistry   2
2   The speed of reactions   4
3   Atoms and the periodic table   6
4   How atoms combine   10
5   Fuels   13
6   Hydrocarbons   17
7   Properties of substances   22
8   Acids and alkalis   26
9   Reactions of acids   29
10   Making electricity   33
11   Metals   37
12   Corrosion   41
13   Plastics   45
14   Fertilisers   49
15   Carbohydrates   54

Part 2   Formulae, Equations and Calculations etc: Examples and Questions   **58**

16   Simple formulae for compounds I   59
17   Simple formulae for compounds II   62
18   Chemical equations   64
19   Balancing chemical equations   66
20   Ionic formulae for compounds   70
21   Ionic and ion-electron equations   72
22   Formula mass and the mole   74
23   Calculations based on balanced equations   76
24   Concentration and the mole   78
25   Calculations based on titration results   80
26   Percentage composition by mass   82
27   Empirical formulae   84
28   Types of chemical formulae   86
29   Types of chemical reaction   88
30   Identification tests   90

Part 1 Answers   **92**

Part 2 Answers   **102**

Introduction

The format of this book is such that it should provide a useful revision aid both for normal classroom use and for the individual student working alone. The Standard Grade Chemistry course has been split into two parts in order to make the material more accessible. In the first part the main theory of the course is dealt with, presented as the usual 15 topics. For each topic revision notes are given covering essential theory, along with questions covering knowledge and understanding as well as problem solving. Answers are given for all questions so that the student receives instant feed-back. Formulae, calculations, etc. are in a second separate part. This helps the flow of information in Part 1 and enables the student to access more easily material which cuts across the course, or is found at various points in it, such as reaction types and chemical tests.

In both text and questions the level of the material is clearly indicated as being either General or Credit. Credit material is clearly flagged with the following sign: **C**

Intermediate 1 material is shown in the text with a ❖ bullet point.

The integrated nature of this book makes it a highly useful revision aid. It provides more than a text which simply gives revision notes, as the questions enable the student to know immediately whether he or she has understood the particular point in question.

Notes to the student

Data booklets

Throughout the text reference has been made to the booklet that is provided by the Scottish Qualifications Authority for use during Standard Grade Chemistry examinations. Candidates will find that it is very beneficial to be thoroughly familiar with its contents. It is available from Robert Gibson and Sons Ltd, 17 Fitzroy Place, Glasgow, G3 7SF.

Litres and cubic decimetres

The units of volume used in this booklet are cubic centimetres (cm^3) and litres. If, as seems likely, there is a move to replace the litre by the cubic decimetre, the reader should note the following:

$$1 \ dm^3 = 1 \ litre \ (l) = 1000 \ cm^3$$

part 1 Topic by Topic: Summaries & Questions

1 Introducing chemistry

Some everyday chemical reactions
fuels burning
iron rusting
copper corroding
wine fermenting
dough rising
bread toasting
cakes baking
eggs frying
food digesting
indigestion remedies acting

- In **all** chemical reactions new substances are formed.
- In **many** chemical reactions there is a change in appearance.
- In **many** chemical reactions there is a detectable energy change.

Elements

- Everything is made from about 100 **elements**.
- Elements cannot be broken down into simpler substances.
- There is a different **symbol** for every element.
- ❖ Some elements, including gold, silver and copper have been known for a long time.
- ❖ Plutonium and some other elements have been made by scientists recently.
- ❖ Some elements, such as gold and silver, are found uncombined, but most are found combined with other elements.
- ❖ Many elements have everyday uses, e.g. copper for water pipes and aluminium for cooking foil.

Compounds

- Compounds are formed when elements react together.
- Compounds with the ending **-ide** usually contain **two** elements.
- Compounds with the ending **-ite** or **-ate** usually contain **three** elements, one of which is oxygen.
- To separate the elements in a compound requires a chemical reaction.

Mixtures

- Mixtures are formed when two or more substances are mingled together without reacting. Examples include air and crude oil.
- Separating the substances in a mixture does **not** involve a chemical reaction.

Solvents, solutes and solutions

- A **solvent** is a liquid in which a substance dissolves.
- A **solute** is a substance that dissolves in a liquid.
- A **solution** is a liquid with something dissolved in it.
- A **dilute** solution is one with little solute compared to the amount of solvent.
- A **concentrated** solution is one with a lot of solute compared to the amount of solvent.
- A **solution** is formed when a **solute** dissolves in a **solvent**.
- **Water** is the most common **solvent**.
- ❖ A **saturated solution** is one in which no more solute can be dissolved at a given temperature.

1 If a piece of aluminium foil is held under mercury and scratched with a sharp object, something unusual happens to it when it is removed. Almost immediately a white substance appears to grow up from the scratch marks, soon reaching a centimetre in height. As this happens the foil becomes distinctly warm. What evidence is there that a chemical reaction has taken place?

2

A	**B**	**C**
water evaporating	apples rotting	fat melting
D	**E**	**F**
electric light bulbs glowing	candles burning	guitar strings vibrating

Which *two* boxes describe a chemical reaction?

3 The first 20 elements (hydrogen to calcium) in the periodic table were all discovered before the twentieth century began. Use the data booklet to help you answer the following questions about these elements.

  a) Which two elements were known in prehistoric times?
  b) Which elements were discovered in the 18th century?
  c) Which was the last of the first 20 elements to be discovered?

4 In some cases the symbol for an element is simply the first letter of the name. With the help of the data booklet, give the element names for each of these symbols:

  a) H b) O c) N d) F e) P f) S g) I
  h) U i) V

5 Complete the following tables:

  a)

Compound	Elements present	
hydrogen oxide	hydrogen	oxygen
lead chloride	_____	_____
sodium sulphide	_____	_____
calcium _____	_____	bromine

  b)

Compound	Elements present		
lithium sulphate	lithium	sulphur	oxygen
zinc carbonate	_____	_____	_____
_____ nitrate	copper	_____	_____
_____ sulphite	barium	_____	_____
potassium nitrite	_____	_____	_____

6 A solution is a mixture formed when one or more solutes dissolves in a solvent. Give five examples of this type of mixture that might be found in the average home.

7 Lager and whisky are both mainly water containing dissolved alcohol. Lager contains about 5% alcohol, whereas whisky contains about 40% alcohol.

A	**B**
solvent	dilute solution
C	**D**
concentrated solution	solute

  a) Which term best describes the alcohol in these liquids?
  b) Which term best describes whisky?

The speed of reactions

Chemical reactions are speeded up by:

- decreasing **particle size**
- increasing **temperature**
- increasing **concentration**
- the presence of a **catalyst**.

Examples

- **Particle size:** small marble chips react faster with acid than large ones; sticks burn faster than a log
- **Temperature:** acid reacts faster with marble chips at a higher temperature; milk goes sour faster at room temperature than in a refrigerator
- **Concentration:** marble chips react faster with concentrated acid than with dilute acid; concentrated bleach acts faster on a stained sink than dilute bleach
- **Catalyst:** manganese(IV) oxide speeds up the decomposition of hydrogen peroxide; platinum (and other transition metals) in car exhaust systems speeds up the conversion of harmful gases into harmless ones

Catalysts are substances that:

- speed up some reactions
- are not used up during reactions
- can be recovered chemically unchanged

- **Enzymes** are biological catalysts.
- ❖ Enzymes are used in making cheese, yoghurt, bread, wine, beer, lager, whisky and biological detergents.

QUESTIONS

1 The grid shows factors that can affect the speed of a chemical reaction.

A	B	C
increase in particle size	increase in concentration	increase in temperature
D	**E**	**F**
decrease in particle size	decrease in concentration	decrease in temperature

Identify the factor responsible for the change in speed of reaction in each of the following examples:

a) Seawater corrodes iron jetties near the Equator more quickly than in northern Scandinavia.
b) Magnesium ribbon burns more slowly than magnesium powder.
c) Two scoops of biological detergent in a washing machine remove stains from clothing more quickly than using one scoop.

2 Zinc metal reacts with acids to give hydrogen gas.

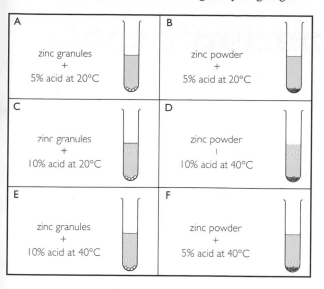

A	B
zinc granules + 5% acid at 20°C	zinc powder + 5% acid at 20°C
C	D
zinc granules + 10% acid at 20°C	zinc powder + 10% acid at 40°C
E	F
zinc granules + 10% acid at 40°C	zinc powder + 5% acid at 40°C

Each of the test tubes contains 1 g of zinc and 10 cm³ of acid. Identify (a) the fastest reaction and (b) the slowest reaction.

3 Copper is a catalyst for the reaction between dilute sulphuric acid and zinc, but only when it is in contact with the zinc.

a) State what is meant by the term 'catalyst'.
b) With the aid of labelled diagrams explain how you would show that copper acts as a catalyst in the way described.

4 Catalysts in car exhaust systems are transition metals.

A	B	C
potassium	platinum	aluminium
D	**E**	**F**
rhodium	strontium	germanium

Use the data booklet to help you identify the *two* metals used in catalytic converters.

5 Richard added 3 g of small (3 mm) marble chips to 10 cm³ of dilute hydrochloric acid using the apparatus shown below:

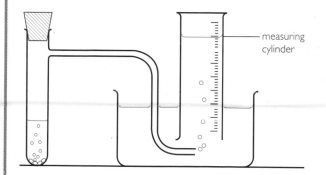

He noted the volume of carbon dioxide produced every 10 s and produced the following graph from his results:

a) What volume of gas was produced during the first 30 s?
b) What volume of gas was produced during the second 30 s?

c) What happened to the speed of the reaction as it proceeded?

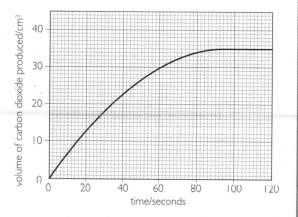

d) Rita repeated the experiment but used 3 g of large (6 mm) marble chips, which she added to 10 cm³ of the same dilute hydrochloric acid. Make a sketch of Richard's graph and add a dotted line to show the graph you think Rita would have obtained.

3 Atoms and the periodic table

- The **periodic table** is how chemists classify elements.
- A column of elements in this table is called a **group**.
- Elements in the same group have similar chemical properties.
- Important groups include: Group 1 – **alkali metals** (reactive)
  Group 7 – **halogens** (reactive non-metals)
  Group 0 – **noble gases** (very unreactive)
- The **transition metals** are an important block of elements between groups 2 and 3.
- Most elements are solids, a few are gases and two, bromine and mercury, are liquids.

Atoms

- Every element is made up of small particles called **atoms**.
- Atoms of different elements are different.
- Atoms of different elements are given a different number called the **atomic number**.
- The atoms of different elements differ in size and mass.

Atomic structure

- All atoms have an extremely small positively charged central part called the **nucleus**.
- Negatively charged particles, called **electrons**, move around outside the nucleus.
- All atoms are electrically neutral because the positive charge of the nucleus is equal to the sum of the negative charges of the electrons.
- Electrons are arranged in special layers around each nucleus. Electron arrangements are given in the data booklet.
- Elements with the same number of outer electrons have similar chemical properties.
- Elements in the same group have the same number of outer electrons (and are therefore chemically similar).

Protons, neutrons, mass numbers, etc.   C

- The nucleus of every atom is positively charged due to the presence of **protons**.
- The atoms of different elements have different numbers of protons.
- Almost all atoms have **neutrons**, which have no charge, in their nucleus.

continued

- Protons and neutrons are much heavier than electrons.

Particle	Charge	Relative mass
proton	+1	1
neutron	0	1
electron	−1	(almost) 0

- The number of protons in the atoms of a particular element is fixed.
- The number of neutrons in the atoms of an element can vary.
- Most elements are made up of more than one kind of atom.
- The **atomic number** of an atom is the number of protons in its nucleus.
- The **mass number** of an atom is the total number of protons and neutrons in its nucleus.
- **Isotopes** are atoms of the same element that have different numbers of neutrons. They have the same atomic number but different mass numbers.
- For any isotope, a special symbol can be written to show its mass number and atomic number, e.g.:

$$\text{mass number} \rightarrow \quad {}^{14}_{6}\text{C}$$
$$\text{atomic number} \rightarrow$$

- Electrons move around the nucleus in **energy levels**, which are also called **shells**.
- Simple **ions** are atoms that possess a positive charge due to electron loss or a negative charge due to electron gain, for example:
  a) the ion ${}^{23}_{11}\text{Na}^+$ has 11 protons, but only 10 electrons
  b) the ion ${}^{32}_{16}\text{S}^{2-}$ has 16 protons, but has 18 electrons.

Relative atomic mass

- The **relative atomic mass** of an element is the average of the mass numbers of its isotopes, taking into account the proportions of each.
- The relative atomic mass of an element is rarely a whole number.

1 The diagram shows a part of the periodic table. The letters used do *not* represent chemical symbols.

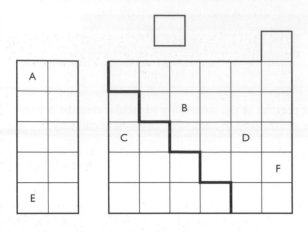

a) Identify the noble gas.
b) Identify the halogen.
c) Identify the *two* elements with the same number of outer electrons.
d) Identify the element in Group 5.

2 Over 100 elements are known. Six are shown below.

A	**B**	**C**
krypton	bromine	oxygen
D	**E**	**F**
carbon	iron	calcium

a) Identify the transition metal.
b) Identify the element with electron arrangement (2,6)
c) Identify the liquid non-metal.
d) Identify the element with atomic number 20.
e) Identify the element that is very unreactive.

3 Copy and complete the following sentences:
The _____ _____ is an arrangement of all the elements in order of increasing _____ number. Elements that have the same number of outer _____ are found in the same _____ .
Elements that have the same number of _____ electrons have _____ chemical properties.

4 All atoms are electrically neutral and yet they contain charged particles.

a) Where in an atom is the positive charge found?
b) Name the particles which carry the negative charge.
c) Explain why, overall, atoms are electrically neutral.

5 Use the data booklet to help you answer these questions:

a) Which of the following are metals and which are non-metals:
(i) thallium (ii) polonium (iii) tellurium?
b) Which of the following do not occur naturally either as the element or in a compound:
(i) protactinium (ii) astatine (iii) francium?
c) Which of the alkali metals would be a liquid on a hot summer's day when the temperature reached 30°C?
d) Give the electron arrangements of:
(i) boron (ii) phosphorus (iii) calcium.
e) How many outer electrons do atoms of oxygen and sulphur have?
f) Which noble gas does not have eight outer electrons in its atoms?

6 Silicon was discovered before germanium.

a) During which year was silicon discovered? (Refer to the data booklet for the answer.)

The properties of germanium and its compounds were accurately predicted before its discovery because of its chemical similarity to silicon.

b) By reference to the periodic table explain why these predictions were possible.

7

A	Number of protons in an atom
B	Number of neutrons in an atom
C	Number of electrons in an atom
D	Number of protons and neutrons in an atom
E	Number of outermost electrons in an atom
F	Group number in the periodic table

Which *two* boxes contain numbers that:

a)   are both equal to the atomic number of an atom?

b)   are equal to the mass number of an atom when added together?

c)   are both equal to 4 for carbon atoms?

d)   change from one isotope of an element to another?

8 Use the information in the data booklet to find the missing terms in the table below.

Element	Symbol	Atomic number	Electron arrangement
beryllium	Be	4	2,2
(a)	Ge	(b)	(c)
(d)	(e)	38	(f)

9 With the help of the information in the data booklet, find the missing terms in the table below. (Each line refers to a different atom.)

Isotope	Mass number	Atomic number	Number of protons	Number of neutrons	Number of electrons
$^3_1$H	3	1	1	2	1
$^{14}_6$C	(a)	(b)	(c)	(d)	(e)
(f)	21	(g)	(h)	(i)	10
(j)	(k)	(l)	26	30	(m)

10 With the help of the information in the data booklet, find the missing terms in the table below. (Each line refers to a different ion.)

Ion	Number of protons	Number of neutrons	Number of electrons
$^7_3$Li$^+$	3	4	2
$^{39}_{19}$K$^+$	(a)	(b)	(c)
(d)	12	13	10

11 With the help of the information in the data booklet, find the missing terms in the table below. (Each line refers to a different ion.)

Ion	Number of protons	Number of neutrons	Number of electrons
$^{17}_8$O^{2-}	8	9	10
$^{79}_{35}$Br$^-$	(a)	(b)	(c)
(d)	15	16	18

12 Copper consists of two isotopes, ^{63}Cu and ^{65}Cu. The relative atomic mass of copper is 63.5. Explain which of these isotopes is present in the greater amount.

13 Bromine consists of two isotopes, ^{79}Br (50.5%) and ^{81}Br (49.5%). Data booklets usually give the approximate value for the relative atomic mass of bromine as 80. Is the accurate value just above or just below 80? Explain your answer.

How atoms combine

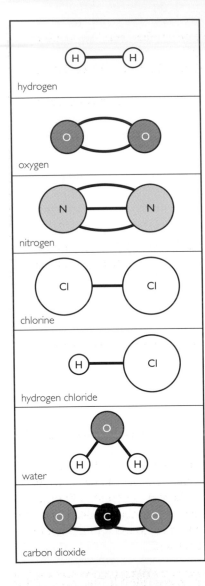

Molecular models of molecules

- Only the noble gases exist as individual atoms not bonded to other atoms.
- In all other substances atoms are held together by **bonds**.
- Atoms in substances containing only **non-metals** are usually held together by **covalent** bonds.
- Groups of atoms held together by covalent bonds are called **molecules**.
- **Diatomic** molecules contain only two atoms.
- A **single** covalent bond is a pair of electrons shared between two atoms.
- Molecules of hydrogen, the halogens and the hydrogen halides all contain single covalent bonds, e.g. H—H, Cl—Cl, H—Cl, etc.
- A **double** covalent bond consists of two shared pairs of electrons, e.g. oxygen, O=O.
- A **triple** covalent bond is present in a nitrogen molecule, N≡N.
- **Molecular formulae** show the number of atoms of the different elements present in a molecule, e.g. H_2, Cl_2, HCl, H_2O, CO_2, etc.
- Covalent bonds are strong, but the forces between molecules are weak. As a result, molecular substances are either gases, liquids or low melting point solids.
- **State symbols** can be used to indicate the state of a substance:
  (g) = gas, (l) = liquid, (s) = solid, (aq) = aqueous (i.e. dissolved in water).

A closer look at covalent bonding

- When atoms bond covalently, they usually share electrons in such a way as to obtain the electron arrangement of a noble gas.
- A **covalent bond** is the result of two positive nuclei being held together by their common attraction for a shared pair of electrons.

Examples

- When two hydrogen atoms share one electron with each other, both obtain the electron arrangement of the noble gas helium:

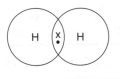

continued

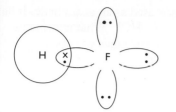

A covalent bond between a hydrogen atom and a fluorine atom

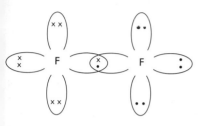

A covalent bond between two fluorine atoms

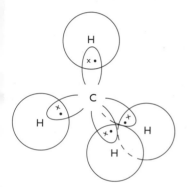

The tetrahedral shape of the methane molecule

- When a hydrogen atom and a fluorine atom share one electron with each other, hydrogen obtains the electron arrangement of helium and fluorine that of neon (see top diagram on left).
- When two fluorine atoms share one electron with each other, each atom obtains the electron arrangement of neon (see middle diagram on left).

The shape of molecules

- Repulsion between the pairs of electrons in the 'lobes' surrounding atoms gives molecules various shapes.
- In many cases the shape is **tetrahedral**, e.g. methane (see bottom diagram on left).
- A **perspective formula** shows the shape of a methane molecule:

- Many molecules are based on a tetrahedral shape, but non-bonded outer electron pairs are not shown in the final molecular shape, e.g. water 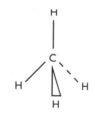 and ammonia:

QUESTIONS

1 Carbon monoxide is a poisonous gas which exists as diatomic molecules.

a) What is meant by the term 'diatomic molecule'?
b) Give the molecular formula for carbon monoxide.

2 Six compounds are shown below.

A	B	C
NaCl	$CaCl_2$	SO_2
D	**E**	**F**
PCl_3	LiF	MgS

Identify the *two* compounds that contain covalent bonding.

3 Fluorine has the molecular formula F_2. The structure of a fluorine molecule can be shown by the formula F—F, where F represents a fluorine atom and — represents a covalent bond. Copy and complete the table to give similar information for the other substances listed.

Substance	Molecular formula	Structure of molecule
fluorine	F_2	F—F
bromine		
hydrogen fluoride		
hydrogen bromide		

4   The sugar glucose has the molecular formula $C_6H_{12}O_6$.

   a) Which elements are present in glucose?
   b) Which type of bonds hold the atoms together in a glucose molecule?
   c) How many atoms are present in one glucose molecule?
   d) How many atoms are present in eight glucose molecules?

5   Chloroform was once used as an anaesthetic. It has the molecular formula $CHCl_3$. What information does this molecular formula give you about molecules of chloroform?

6   Draw diagrams to show how the outer electrons are shared to form the covalent bond(s) in molecules of:

   a) iodine
   b) hydrogen iodide
   c) hydrogen sulphide
   d) nitrogen trichloride, NCl_3
   e) tetrachloromethane, CCl_4.

Identify the shape that could represent a molecule of:

   a) hydrogen sulphide
   b) hydrogen chloride
   c) carbon dioxide
   d) ammonia
   e) fluorine
   f) methane.

7   A main group element X is known to bond covalently with fluorine to form a compound with molecular formula XF_2. In this compound both X and fluorine obtain noble gas electron arrangements by sharing electrons.

   a) To which main group of the periodic table is element X likely to belong?
   b) Draw a diagram to show how the outer electrons are shared to form the covalent bonds in a molecule of XF_2.
   c) Which noble gas does fluorine achieve the electron arrangement of in the compound XF_2?

9   Draw perspective formulae (i.e. those giving symbols and covalent bonds that show the true shapes of the molecules) for:

   a) water
   b) hydrogen iodide
   c) carbon disulphide
   d) nitrogen trichloride
   e) tetrafluoromethane, CF_4
   f) silane, SiH_4.

8   Molecules can have various shapes, some of which are shown below. (The letters X, Y, Z and Q do not represent any particular element.)

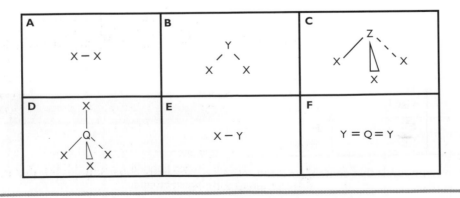

Fuels

- A **fuel** is a substance that gives out energy when it burns.
- An **exothermic** reaction is one in which heat energy is released.
- When a substance burns it reacts with oxygen.
- Oxygen makes up about one fifth of the air (the rest is mainly nitrogen).
- The test for oxygen is that it re-lights a glowing splint.
- **Combustion** is another word for burning.

Coal, oil and natural gas

- Coal, oil and natural gas are **fossil fuels**, formed millions of years ago.
- A **fossil fuel** is one that has been formed from the remains of living things.
- Coal was formed from plant material, including trees.
- Oil and natural gas were formed from tiny sea creatures and plants.
- The fossil fuels are **finite** resources as they are limited in amount and cannot be replaced.
- ❖ Over-use of fossil fuels may lead to a fuel crisis.
- Oil spillages can cause great damage to marine wildlife and the environment.
- Oil requires a complex process of **refining** before it can be used.

Fractional distillation of crude oil

- Crude oil is a mixture of carbon compounds.
- The carbon compounds in crude oil are mainly **hydrocarbons**.
- **Hydrocarbons** are compounds containing only carbon and hydrogen.
- **Fractional distillation** is used to separate crude oil into **fractions**.
- A **fraction** is a group of compounds with boiling points within a given range:

Fraction	Boiling range/°C	Carbon atoms per molecule	End-uses
gas	−160–20	1–4	fuel gases
gasoline	20–65	5–6	petrol and
naphtha	65–180	6–11	petrochemicals
kerosene	180–250	9–15	heating/jet fuel
gas oils	250–350	15–25	diesel fuel
residue	>350	>25	bitumen, wax, etc.

- The fractions vary in **viscosity** (how 'thick' it is), **flammability** and **ease of vaporisation**:

Fraction	Gas	Gasoline	Naphtha	Kerosene	Gas oil	Residue
molecular size			increasing →			
boiling range			increasing →			
viscosity			increasing →			
flammability	←		increasing			
vaporisability	←		increasing			

Explanation of variations

- Boiling range and viscosity increase with increasing molecular size because the forces between molecules also increase.
- Vaporisation and flammability are also linked to molecular size. The smaller the molecules, the weaker are the forces between them and, as a result, they vaporise more readily.

❖ There are competing demands for crude oil. For example, naphtha is used to make petrol, but it is also needed for the manufacture of consumer products such as textiles, dyes, plastics, detergents, etc.

Fuels and combustion

- Many fuels contain carbon and hydrogen. When burned completely they produce carbon dioxide and water.
- The test for carbon dioxide is that it turns lime water milky.
- The test for water is that it freezes at 0°C and boils at 100°C.

- The production of carbon dioxide and water on combustion indicates the presence of **carbon** and **hydrogen** in the original fuel. This is because there is no carbon and hydrogen in the air so the carbon and hydrogen in the products must come from the original fuel.

- Incomplete combustion of a carbon-containing fuel can produce carbon and carbon monoxide.
- Carbon monoxide is a poisonous gas.

Pollution caused by combustion of fuels

- Burning fossil fuels produces carbon dioxide, a 'greenhouse' gas that causes global warming.
- Some fuels contain sulphur, which produces poisonous sulphur dioxide when burned. Most sulphur is removed from crude oil and natural gas during refining and processing.
- In petrol engines, and to a lesser extent in diesel engines, nitrogen and oxygen combine to form poisonous oxides of nitrogen, including nitrogen dioxide.
- Lead compounds, which are added to some forms of petrol, cause pollution.
❖ Benzene fumes from unleaded petrol are toxic.

❖ Soot particles produced by the incomplete combustion of diesel are harmful.
- Air pollution from the burning of hydrocarbons can be reduced by the use of special exhaust systems that convert pollutant gases into harmless gases.
- Decreasing the fuel-to-air ratio in car engines also reduces pollution.

- All new cars are now fitted with **catalytic converters**.
- These convert oxides of nitrogen into nitrogen and oxygen.
- They change unburnt hydrocarbons and carbon monoxide into water and carbon dioxide.
- **'Lean burn'** engines have a lower fuel-to-air ratio, which improves efficiency because it leads to more complete combustion.
- A lower fuel-to-air ratio reduces pollution because there are fewer unburnt hydrocarbons and less carbon monoxide in the exhaust gases.

QUESTIONS

1 Fractions from the distillation of crude oil are shown in the grid.

A	B	C
gases	gasoline	naphtha
D	**E**	**F**
kerosene	gas oils	residue

Identify the fraction that:

a) is used to provide fuel for jet aircraft
b) is used to provide bitumen for road surfaces

---

c) contains molecules that have three carbon atoms in them
d) contains molecules that have thirty carbon atoms in them.

---

2 Most of the fractions from crude oil consist of liquid hydrocarbons. The size of hydrocarbon molecules varies considerably from one fraction to another.

a) For the liquid hydrocarbons:
   (i) State what happens to flammability as molecular size increases.
   (ii) State what happens to viscosity as molecular size increases.

b) State what is meant by 'viscosity'.

---

c) Explain the change in viscosity stated in (a)(ii) above.

---

3 a) State one way in which the formation processes of coal and crude oil are different.
   b) Coal and crude oil are known to be causes of pollution. Give two examples of pollution for each substance.

4 Despite efforts to remove them, some sulphur compounds are still present in both petrol and diesel used by motor vehicles. One such compound is:

$$\text{H}-\overset{\displaystyle \overset{\text{H}}{|}}{\underset{\displaystyle \underset{\text{H}}{|}}{\text{C}}}-\overset{\displaystyle \overset{\text{H}}{|}}{\underset{\displaystyle \underset{\text{H}}{|}}{\text{C}}}-\text{S}-\text{H}$$

a) Name *all* the products of the complete combustion of this compound.
b) Explain why the burning of this compound would cause pollution.

5 Many substances can be used as fuels. Some are shown in the table below.

Fuel	Energy released on burning 1 g of fuel/kJ
hydrogen	143
methane	56
petrol	48
ethanol	30
carbon monoxide	10

a) Present this information as a bar graph.
b) What is meant by the word 'fuel'?
c) Which of these fuels would produce no carbon dioxide on burning?
d) Which fuel might be rejected for use because it is a highly poisonous gas?

C

6 Three transition metals, platinum, palladium and rhodium, are used in catalytic converters in car exhaust systems. Rhodium is the key element in catalysing the reaction between carbon monoxide and nitrogen monoxide to give two non-poisonous gases.

a) Suggest what these two less harmful gases might be.
b) Give a balanced equation for the reaction.

7 At 300°C about 90% of the pollutant gases in car exhausts are converted into less harmful gases on passage through a catalytic converter, even though this takes only one tenth of a second. However, it is believed that during most in-town journeys the catalytic converter, even in excellent condition, hardly changes any pollutant gases into harmless ones. Offer an explanation for this apparent failure.

Hydrocarbons

Alkanes

- The **alkanes** (a subset of the set of hydrocarbons) are the main constituents of natural gas and crude oil. The eight simplest are:

Name	Molecular formula and state	Shortened structural formula
methane	$CH_4(g)$	CH_4
ethane	$C_2H_6(g)$	CH_3CH_3
propane	$C_3H_8(g)$	$CH_3CH_2CH_3$
butane	$C_4H_{10}(g)$	$CH_3CH_2CH_2CH_3$
pentane	$C_5H_{12}(l)$	$CH_3CH_2CH_2CH_2CH_3$
hexane	$C_6H_{14}(l)$	$CH_3CH_2CH_2CH_2CH_2CH_3$
heptane	$C_7H_{16}(l)$	$CH_3CH_2CH_2CH_2CH_2CH_2CH_3$
octane	$C_8H_{18}(l)$	$CH_3CH_2CH_2CH_2CH_2CH_2CH_2CH_3$

- The **general formula** for the alkanes is C_nH_{2n+2}.
- Full structural formulae are often used for the alkanes, e.g.

methane   propane

- The simpler alkanes are mainly used as fuels, but there are competing demands from the petrochemicals industry, e.g. all of the ethane is used to make polythene, antifreeze, polyester fibres, etc.
- The alkanes burn to give carbon dioxide and water on complete combustion.
- The alkanes are said to be **saturated** because they contain only single C—C bonds.
- The alkanes do not react with bromine solution in the test for unsaturation.

Alkenes

- The **alkenes** (a subset of the set of hydrocarbons) are similar to the alkanes, but contain a double C=C bond, indicated by the **-ene** name ending. Examples include:

Name	Molecular formula and state	Shortened structural formula
ethene	C_2H_4(g)	$CH_2\!=\!CH_2$
propene	C_3H_6(g)	$CH_3CH\!=\!CH_2$
hexene	C_6H_{12}(l)	$CH_3CH_2CH_2CH_2CH\!=\!CH_2$

- The **general formula** for the alkenes is C_nH_{2n}.
- Full structural formulae are often used for the alkenes.
- The alkenes burn to give carbon dioxide and water on complete combustion.
- The presence of the $C\!=\!C$ bond makes the alkenes more reactive than the alkanes.
- The alkenes undergo many **addition** reactions, e.g.

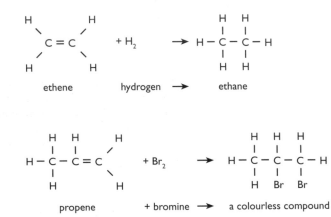

- The alkenes are said to be **unsaturated** because they contain a double $C\!=\!C$ bond.
- Alkenes decolourise bromine solution in the test for unsaturation.

Cracking

- Fractional distillation of crude oil gives more long-chain hydrocarbons (mainly alkanes) than are useful for industrial purposes.
- **Cracking** is a method of producing smaller, more useful molecules by heating large hydrocarbon molecules in the presence of a catalyst.
- ❖ Cracking can be carried out in the laboratory using an aluminium oxide or silicate catalyst.
- Cracking alkane molecules usually produces a mixture of smaller alkanes and alkenes.

> - There are insufficient hydrogen atoms in an alkane molecule for it to produce only smaller alkanes on cracking.
> - The presence of a catalyst, such as aluminium oxide, allows the cracking process to take place at a lower temperature, thus making it more economical.

Cycloalkanes

- The **cycloalkanes** (a subset of the set of hydrocarbons) are similar to the alkanes in that they are saturated and contain only single C—C bonds. They are ring molecules. The two simplest are:

Name	Molecular formula and state	Shortened structural formula
cyclopropane	$C_3H_6(g)$	$$CH_2$$ $$\diagup \; \diagdown$$ $$CH_2 — CH_2$$
cyclobutane	$C_4H_8(g)$	$$CH_2 — CH_2$$ $$\mid \qquad \mid$$ $$CH_2 — CH_2$$

- The **general formula** for the cycloalkanes is C_nH_{2n}.
- Full structural formulae are often used for the cycloalkanes.
- The cycloalkanes burn to give carbon dioxide and water on complete combustion.
- Since they are saturated, the cycloalkanes do not decolourise bromine solution.

Homologous series

The alkanes, alkenes and cycloalkanes are examples of **homologous series**, being groups of compounds which:

- can be represented by a general formula
- have similar chemical properties
- show a gradual change in physical properties, such as boiling points.

Isomers

- **Isomers** are compounds that have the same molecular formula but have different structural formulae, e.g. there are two isomers with molecular formula C_4H_{10}:

continued

> • For every cycloalkane there is an alkene that is an isomer, e.g. propene and cyclopropane both have the molecular formula C_3H_6:
>
>
> • There are no isomers for methane (CH_4), ethane (C_2H_6), propane (C_3H_8) and ethene (C_2H_4).

QUESTIONS

1 Full structural formulae for some hydrocarbons are given in the grid below.

a) Which *two* hydrocarbons belong to a series with the general formula C_nH_{2n+2}?
b) Which hydrocarbon is the simplest alkene?

c) Which *two* hydrocarbons are isomers?

2 a) Draw the full structural formula for butane.
b) Draw the shortened structural formula for pentene.
c) Give the molecular formula for the alkane with 21 carbon atoms in each molecule.
d) Give the molecular formula for the alkene with 16 hydrogen atoms in each molecule.
e) Give the empirical formula for all alkenes.

3 a) Name the compound produced when hexene reacts with hydrogen.
b) Name the compound that would react with hydrogen to give pentane.

4 a) Explain the meaning of the term 'unsaturated hydrocarbon'.
b) A liquid is thought to be an unsaturated hydrocarbon. Describe the chemical test which should be carried out to investigate this and describe the result obtained if the test is positive.

5 Write an equation for the reaction between ethene and bromine using full structural formulae.

6 Draw full structural formulae for the molecules produced when (a) buta-1,3-diene and (b) cycloocta-1,3,5,7-tetraene react *completely* with bromine solution.

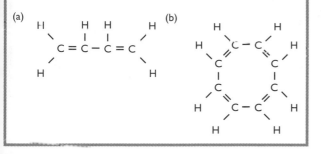

7 a) As part of crude oil refining, some fractions are subjected to the process known as cracking. What is meant by the term 'cracking'?

b) Fractional distillation of crude oil separates it into a variety of groups of mainly hydrocarbon molecules. Why then is the process of cracking needed as well?

8 The cracking of a single alkane was found to produce only butene and ethane.

a) Which alkane was being cracked?

b) Why could the cracking process not result in the formation of two alkane molecules?

9 Compound X is both a feedstock for the petrochemicals industry and a fuel which is widely used in rural areas. The cracking of X produced only propene and hydrogen.

a) Name compound X and give an equation for the cracking reaction using molecular formulae.

b) Why would the use of a catalyst during the cracking reaction make the process more economical?

10 Two isomers with the molecular formula C_4H_{10} were given on page 19. Draw full structural formulae for the isomers with molecular formula C_6H_{14}.

7 Properties of substances

Ionic bonding

- Compounds of metals and non-metals contain **ionic bonding**.
- Metal atoms lose electrons to form positively charged ions, e.g. Na^+.
- Non-metal atoms gain electrons to form negatively charged ions, e.g. Cl^-.
- Ionic compounds, such as sodium chloride, exist as giant lattices of ions.
- An **ionic bond** is the electrostatic force of attraction between oppositely charged ions.

> **C**
> - Ionic bonds are strong, giving ionic compounds high melting points.

- Ionic compounds do not conduct electricity in the solid state because the ions are not free to move.
- Ionic compounds do conduct electricity when molten or dissolved in water because the ions can then move.
- An **electrolyte** is a substance that conducts due to the movement of ions.
- When ionic compounds conduct, chemical changes take place at the electrodes. This process is called **electrolysis**.
- Electrolysis of a molten ionic compound, made up of positive metal ions and negative non-metal ions, results in the metal being produced at the negative electrode and the non-metal being produced at the positive electrode.

> **C**
> - Electrolysis of molten lead(II) bromide produces lead and bromine:
>
> $$Pb^{2+} + 2e \rightarrow Pb$$
> $$2Br^- \rightarrow Br_2 + 2e$$
>
> - A d.c. (direct current) supply must be used for electrolysis experiments otherwise the sign of the electrode constantly changes and as a result the electrode products cannot be identified.

- The literal meaning of 'electrolysis' is 'breaking up by means of electricity'.
- Electrolysis of solutions of certain ionic compounds can also result in them being broken up.

- Electrolysis of copper(II) chloride solution produces copper and chlorine:

$$Cu^{2+} + 2e \rightarrow Cu$$
$$2Cl^- \rightarrow Cl_2 + 2e$$

- Some ions consist of small groups of atoms joined together, e.g. chromate ions, CrO_4^{2-}.
- The colour of an ionic compound can be related to the colours of the ions present, e.g. sodium chloride is colourless, so sodium and chloride ions must also be colourless but sodium chromate is yellow, so chromate ions must be yellow.
- Ion migration experiments can be used to investigate the charges of coloured ions.

Covalent molecular and covalent network substances

Structures

- Most non-metal elements exist as small molecules – they are **covalent molecular**, e.g. hydrogen, H_2, and bromine, Br_2.
- Carbon exists as diamond and graphite. In these substances a huge number of carbon atoms are held together by a network of covalent bonds – they are **covalent network**.
- Compounds formed between non-metals usually exist as small molecules – they are covalent molecular, e.g. water, H_2O, and carbon dioxide, CO_2.
- Some compounds formed between non-metals are of the covalent network type, e.g. silicon dioxide, SiO_2. (SiO_2 is an empirical formula and not a molecular formula, since it only shows the ratio of atoms present in the structure.)

Properties

- Covalent substances do not conduct electricity in any state as no charged particles are present, only electrically neutral molecules.
- Unlike ionic compounds, which mostly dissolve in water, covalent substances tend to be insoluble in water, but are often soluble in other solvents, e.g. iodine (I_2) is much more soluble in alcohol than in water.

- Covalent molecular substances can be gases, liquids or low melting point solids. This is because the forces of attraction between the molecules are weak.
- Covalent network substances have high melting points. This is because at the melting point strong covalent bonds must be broken.

Conduction of electricity

- An electric current is a flow of charged particles.
- Metals and graphite conduct electricity because some of their electrons are free to move.
- Ions carry an electric current through electrolytes, both molten ionic compounds and solutions of ionic compounds.

QUESTIONS

1   In the table below the following key applies:
    ✓ = conducts electricity
    ✗ = does not conduct electricity.

Substance	Solid state	Liquid state	Solution in water	State at 25°C
A	✓	✓	insoluble	(l)
B	✗	✓	✓	(s)
C	✗	✗	✗	(s)
D	✓	✓	insoluble	(s)
E	✗	✗	insoluble	(l)

Identify the substance which could be:

a) kerosene
b) sugar ($C_{12}H_{22}O_{11}$)
c) tin
d) sodium bromide.

State what the remaining substance might be.

2

A S	B Cl	C Be
D Ba	E C	F Se

Identify:

a) the non-metal in the grid above that conducts electricity
b) the *two* other elements in the grid that conduct electricity by movement of electrons through them.

3

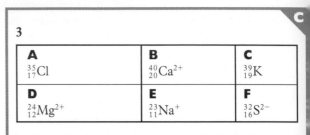

A $^{35}_{17}Cl$	B $^{40}_{20}Ca^{2+}$	C $^{39}_{19}K$
D $^{24}_{12}Mg^{2+}$	E $^{23}_{11}Na^{+}$	F $^{32}_{16}S^{2-}$

Identify the particles in the grid above that have the same electron arrangement as argon.

4

A silicon dioxide	B lead fluoride	C sodium sulphate
D lithium iodide	E nickel chloride	F magnesium oxide

Identify the compound that:

a) contains more than two elements
b) does *not* conduct electricity when molten.

5   Sodium is made industrially by the electrolysis of molten sodium chloride.

a) What is meant by the term 'electrolysis'?
b) Why does solid sodium chloride not conduct electricity?
c) Name the other product of the electrolysis.
d) Why must the two products of the electrolysis be kept apart?

e) Give ion-electron equations for the reactions taking place at (i) the negative electrode and (ii) the positive electrode.

5 Aluminium is made in the Scottish Highlands using electrolysis. Molten aluminium oxide is used but since this does not conduct electricity well, sodium aluminium fluoride is added as an electrolyte.

a) What is meant by the term 'electrolyte'?

b) Give the ion-electron equation for the reaction which takes place at the negative electrode.

7 Solutions of the following ionic compounds were examined and the following observations made:

sodium dichromate	orange
sodium nitrate	colourless
copper nitrate	blue

Crystals of sodium dichromate and copper nitrate were then used in the following ion migration experiment. The directions of colour movements are shown in the diagram on the right.

Explain what conclusions can be reached regarding the colour *and* charge of:

a) the copper ions used in the experiment
b) the dichromate ions used in the experiment.

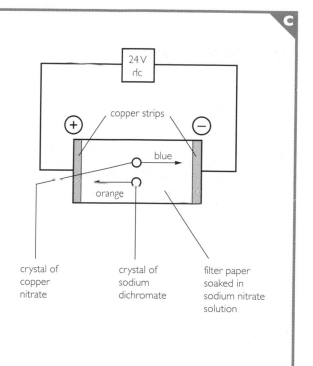

24 V dc

copper strips

+

−

blue

orange

crystal of copper nitrate

crystal of sodium dichromate

filter paper soaked in sodium nitrate solution

Acids and alkalis

The pH scale

- **pH** is a number that indicates the degree of acidity or alkalinity of a solution.

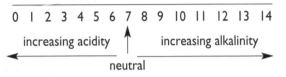

- Universal indicator, pH paper or a pH meter can be used to find the pH of solutions.

- In pure water and all neutral solutions there is a tiny but equal concentration of hydrogen and hydroxide ions, $H^+(aq)$ and $OH^-(aq)$.

- When acids dissolve in water they produce $H^+(aq)$ ions.

- An acidic solution has a higher concentration of $H^+(aq)$ ions than pure water.

- When alkalis dissolve in water they produce $OH^-(aq)$ ions.

- An alkaline solution has a higher concentration of $OH^-(aq)$ ions than pure water.
- Diluting an acidic or alkaline solution with water reduces the concentration of $H^+(aq)$ and $OH^-(aq)$ ions, moving the pH towards 7 in both cases.

- In simple terms:
  diluting an acidic solution with water reduces the acidity and the pH increases towards 7
  diluting an alkaline solution reduces the alkalinity and the pH decreases towards 7.

Some common acids

Name	Simple formula	Ions present in aqueous solution
hydrochloric acid	HCl	$H^+(aq) + Cl^-(aq)$
nitric acid	HNO_3	$H^+(aq) + NO_3^-(aq)$
sulphuric acid	H_2SO_4	$2H^+(aq) + SO_4^{2-}(aq)$

- When a solution of an acid is electrolysed, hydrogen gas is produced at the negative electrode, providing evidence for positively charged hydrogen ions in the solution.

Oxides of non-metals and pollution

- Oxides of non-metals which dissolve in water produce **acidic** solutions, e.g. CO_2, SO_2 and NO_2.
- Sulphur dioxide is the main cause of acid rain. When released, it reacts with water in the air.
- Acid rain: erodes buildings made of limestone, sandstone, marble, etc.
  causes corrosion of iron and steel
  lowers soil pH affecting plant growth
  damages trees
  harms aquatic life.

Oxides and hydroxides of metals

- Metal oxides and hydroxides that dissolve in water produce **alkaline** solutions. The oxides and hydroxides of Group 1 metals are all very soluble. For those in Group 2, solubility increases down the group.
- Soluble metal oxides react with water producing the corresponding metal hydroxide, e.g.

  sodium oxide + water → sodium hydroxide solution

- Lime water is a common laboratory alkali. Its chemical name is calcium hydroxide solution.

Common household acids and alkalis

- **Acids**: vinegar, citrus fruits, cola drinks, etc.
- **Alkalis**: oven cleaner, bleach, bicarbonate of soda, dishwasher powder/liquid, soap, ammonia solution, etc.

1

A	B	C
sodium sulphate	magnesium chloride	potassium nitrate
D	**E**	**F**
calcium oxide	barium carbonate	lithium hydroxide

Identify the compounds in the grid that would produce an alkaline solution when dissolved in water.

2 Jenny noticed that one of the ingredients in a cola drink was phosphoric acid. She set up the following apparatus in the hope of obtaining hydrogen gas at the negative electrode:

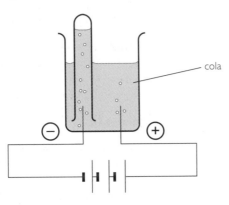

cola

a) Which ion do all acids produce when they dissolve in water?

b) Describe a simple test that would prove if the cola drink was acidic.

c) What test could Jenny carry out on the gas collected in the test tube to show that it was hydrogen?

d) Jenny's teacher told her that when acid solutions are electrolysed the ions attracted to the negative electrode gain electrons and form molecules of hydrogen gas. Write an ion-electron equation for this process.

3 a) Write a word equation for the reaction of lithium oxide with water to give lithium hydroxide.

b) Rewrite the equation using simple chemical formulae.

4 Write a balanced chemical equation for the reaction of calcium oxide with water, showing state symbols.

5 Ammonia is the only common alkaline gas. It is very soluble in water.

a) Which ion must ammonia produce on dissolving in, and reacting with, water?

b) Draw a diagram to show clearly what you would expect to happen when the stopper is removed from the test tube shown below:

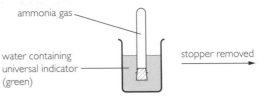

ammonia gas

water containing universal indicator (green)

stopper removed

6 Boracic acid, found in some eye washes, is only slightly acidic. Ethanoic acid, in vinegar, is somewhat more acidic. Citric acid, in citrus fruits, is more acidic still but is also classified as a weak acid. Hydrochloric acid, used to remove rust marks from white enamel, is very acidic. Suggest possible pH values for dilute solutions of these four acids, assuming that they are of roughly equal concentration.

7 Sulphuric acid is used in car batteries. It is so acidic that it has a pH of less than 0. If battery acid is spilled on clothing, adding plenty of water to the spillage is usually recommended as a simple, but effective, first thing to do.

a) What effect does dilution have on the level of acidity of the acid?

b) What is the effect of dilution on the pH of the acid?

c) What effect does dilution have on the hydrogen ion concentration?

8 The simple formula for nitric acid is HNO_3. The ions present in dilute nitric acid are $H^+(aq)$ and $NO_3^-(aq)$. Perchloric acid has the simple formula $HClO_4$. In solution it also exists as ions, one of which is the perchlorate ion. Write the formula for the perchlorate ion in solution.

Reactions of acids

Neutralisation

- **Neutralisation** is a reaction in which the pH of a solution moves towards 7. It is the reaction of acids with **neutralisers**.
- **Neutralisers** include metals, metal oxides, hydroxides, carbonates and hydrogencarbonates, and ammonia.

Everyday examples of neutralisation

- Lime (calcium oxide) is used to reduce acidity in soil and water.
- Cures for acid indigestion contain neutralisers such as calcium carbonate.

Bases and alkalis

- A **base** is a substance that neutralises an acid.
- An **alkali** is a base that dissolves in water.

Salts

- **Salts** are ionic compounds formed in reactions between acids and neutralisers. They contain a metal ion, or an ammonium ion, from the neutraliser and a negative ion from the acid.

Neutraliser	Positive ion/ salt name	Acid	Negative ion/ salt name
sodium hydroxide	sodium ...	hydrochloric acid	... chloride
calcium carbonate	calcium ...	sulphuric acid	... sulphate
ammonia	ammonium ...	nitric acid	... nitrate

- A **salt** is a substance in which the hydrogen ion of an acid has been replaced by a metal ion or an ammonium ion.

Metal hydroxide/acid reactions

metal hydroxide + acid → salt + water

e.g. sodium hydroxide + hydrochloric acid → sodium chloride + water

$$NaOH(aq) + HCl(aq) \rightarrow NaCl(aq) + H_2O(l)$$

i.e. $Na^+(aq) + OH^-(aq) + H^+(aq) + Cl^-(aq) \rightarrow$
$\qquad Na^+(aq) + Cl^-(aq) + H_2O(l)$

Removing spectator ions gives:

$$OH^-(aq) + H^+(aq) \rightarrow H_2O(l)$$

- When acids and metal hydroxides react, hydrogen ions and hydroxide ions join to form water.

Metal oxide/acid reactions

metal oxide + acid → salt + water

e.g. zinc oxide + sulphuric acid → zinc sulphate + water

$\qquad ZnO(s) + H_2SO_4(aq) \rightarrow ZnSO_4(aq) + H_2O(l)$

i.e. $Zn^{2+}O^{2-}(s) + 2H^+(aq) + SO_4^{2-}(aq) \rightarrow$
$\qquad Zn^{2+}(aq) + SO_4^{2-}(aq) + H_2O(l)$

Removing spectator ions gives:

$$O^{2-}(s) + 2H^+(aq) \rightarrow H_2O(l)$$

- When acids and metal oxides react, hydrogen ions and oxide ions join to form water.

Metal carbonate/acid reactions

metal carbonate + acid → salt + water + carbon dioxide

e.g. sodium carbonate + nitric acid → sodium nitrate + water + carbon dioxide

$\qquad Na_2CO_3(aq) + 2HNO_3(aq) \rightarrow 2NaNO_3(aq) + H_2O(l) + CO_2(g)$

i.e. $2Na^+(aq) + CO_3^{2-}(aq) + 2H^+(aq) + 2NO_3^-(aq) \rightarrow$
$\qquad 2Na^+(aq) + 2NO_3^-(aq) + H_2O(l) + CO_2(g)$

Removing spectator ions gives:

$$CO_3^{2-}(aq) + 2H^+(aq) \rightarrow H_2O(l) + CO_2(g)$$

- When acids and carbonates react, hydrogen ions and carbonate ions react to form water and carbon dioxide.

Metal/acid reactions

$$\text{metal} + \text{acid} \rightarrow \text{salt} + \text{hydrogen}$$
(not all metals react)

e.g.   magnesium + sulphuric acid $\rightarrow$ magnesium sulphate + hydrogen

$$Mg(s) + H_2SO_4(aq) \rightarrow MgSO_4(aq) + H_2(g)$$

i.c. $Mg(s) + 2H^+(aq) + SO_4^{2-}(aq) \rightarrow Mg^{2+}(aq) + SO_4^{2-}(aq) + H_2(g)$

Removing spectator ions gives:

$$Mg(s) + 2H^+(aq) \rightarrow Mg^{2+}(aq) + H_2(g)$$

- When acids and metals react, hydrogen ions are turned into hydrogen molecules.

Acid rain reacts with carbonate rocks such as marble and limestone, and with metals such as iron.

Making soluble salts by neutralisation of acids

I   Using alkalis
- Add acid to alkali, using an indicator to show when neutralisation is exact.
- Note the volumes used and mix these volumes **without** indicator.
- Evaporate off some of the water.
- Allow to crystallise.
- Filter off the crystals of salt.

II   Using insoluble bases
- Add insoluble base to acid until no more reacts.
- Filter off the excess.
- Evaporate off some of the water.
- Filter off the crystals of salt.

Making insoluble salts by precipitation

- **Precipitation** is the reaction of two solutions to form an insoluble product called a **precipitate**.
- Insoluble salts can be formed by precipitation.
- Select a soluble compound containing the positive ion of the salt.
- Select a soluble compound containing the negative ion of the salt.
- Mix solutions of the two compounds and filter off the insoluble salt, e.g.

zinc sulphate + sodium carbonate $\rightarrow$ zinc carbonate + sodium sulphate
(soln)   (soln)   (ppt)   (soln)

$$ZnSO_4(aq) + Na_2CO_3(aq) \rightarrow ZnCO_3(s) + Na_2SO_4(aq)$$

Using ionic formulae and removing spectator ions:

$$Zn^{2+}(aq) + CO_3^{2-}(aq) \rightarrow Zn^{2+}CO_3^{2-}(s)$$

1

A	B	C
aluminium hydroxide	barium hydroxide	calcium hydroxide
D	**E**	**F**
lithium hydroxide	potassium hydroxide	zinc hydroxide

With the help of the data booklet identify:

a) the *two* hydroxides which have a solubility of less than 1 g/l

b) the hydroxide which could have a solubility of 5 g/l.

2 Copy and complete the following word equations:

a) lithium hydroxide + hydrochloric acid

$\rightarrow$ _____ + _____

b) aluminium oxide + nitric acid

$\rightarrow$ _____ + _____

c) strontium carbonate + sulphuric acid

$\rightarrow$ _____ + _____ + _____

d) zinc + hydrochloric acid

$\rightarrow$ _____ + _____

3 Copy and complete the following equations in which simple formulae and state symbols have been used. (There is no need to balance the equations.)

a) $Ca(OH)_2(aq) + HCl(aq) \rightarrow$ ____ + ____

b) $CuO(s) +$ ____ $\rightarrow Cu(NO_3)_2(aq) +$ ____

c) ____ $+ H_2SO_4(aq) \rightarrow K_2SO_4(aq) +$ ____ $+ CO_2(g)$

d) $Li(s) +$ ____ $\rightarrow LiCl(aq) +$ ____

4 Indigestion is caused by hydrochloric acid from the stomach. One remedy for indigestion contains calcium carbonate, another magnesium hydroxide.

a) Give word equations for the reaction of these two neutralisers with hydrochloric acid.

b) Give the same two equations using simple chemical formulae instead of words.

c) Balance the equations and rewrite them using ionic formulae, where appropriate, and state symbols.

5 a) When an alkaline metal hydroxide solution and an acid react which two ions combine to produce water molecules?

b) When a metal carbonate and an acid react which two ions combine to produce water and carbon dioxide molecules?

6 a) Nickel(II) oxide is a black insoluble solid. Explain how you would carry out an experiment using nickel(II) oxide and dilute sulphuric acid to make crystals of nickel(II) sulphate.

b) Give an equation, using simple chemical formulae and state symbols, for the reaction taking place.

7 Given sodium hydroxide solution, dilute nitric acid and any other chemicals or apparatus you require, explain how you would make crystals of sodium nitrate.

8 Use the table of solubilities in the data booklet to help you complete the following equations using simple formulae and state symbols:

a) $BaCl_2(aq) + K_2SO_4(aq) \rightarrow BaSO_4(s) +$ ____

b) $CuSO_4(aq) + Na_2CO_3(aq) \rightarrow$ ____ + ____

c) $AgNO_3(aq) + LiCl(aq) \rightarrow$ ____ + ____

9 Using ionic formulae and removing spectator ions, the equation in question 8(a) can be rewritten as:

$$Ba^{2+}(aq) + SO_4^{2-}(aq) \rightarrow Ba^{2+}SO_4^{2-}(s)$$

Write similar equations for questions 8(b) and 8(c).

Making electricity

Batteries and cells

- A **chemical cell** converts chemical energy into electrical energy.
- A **battery** is two or more cells joined together.
- Chemicals are used up when cells produce electricity.
- Some cells are rechargeable, e.g. in a 'lead-acid' car battery.
- In a cell one substance gives up electrons, another accepts them.
- An **electrolyte** completes the circuit in a cell.
- Compared to mains electricity, batteries of cells are safer and portable but more expensive and greater users of finite resources such as zinc, lead, nickel, etc.

Metals and the electrochemical series (ECS)

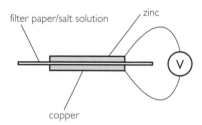

A simple cell

- A cell can consist of two different metals and an electrolyte.
- Different metals produce different voltages.
- The higher a metal is in the ECS, the more readily it loses electrons.
- The further apart two metals are in the ECS, the greater is the cell voltage.
- In a cell, electrons flow from the metal higher in the ECS to the one lower down through the wires and meter.

Displacement and the ECS

- A **displacement** reaction involves the formation of a metal, from a solution of its ions, by reaction with a metal higher in the ECS, e.g.

$$Zn(s) + CuSO_4(aq) \rightarrow Cu(s) + ZnSO_4(aq)$$

- The metal doing the displacing loses electrons and forms ions,

$$Zn(s) \rightarrow Zn^{2+}(aq) + 2e \quad (\textbf{oxidation} = \text{loss of electrons})$$

- The ions of the metal being displaced gain electrons and form metal atoms, e.g.

$$2e + Cu^{2+}(aq) \rightarrow Cu(s) \quad (\textbf{reduction} = \text{gain of electrons})$$

- Displacement reactions are **redox** processes since they involve both loss and gain of electrons, e.g.

$$Zn(s) + Cu^{2+}(aq) \rightarrow Zn^{2+}(aq) + Cu(s)$$

continued

- The reaction of metals and acids can be used to position **hydrogen** in the ECS.
- Only those metals **above** hydrogen in the ECS displace it from an acid, e.g.

$$Zn(s) + 2H^+(aq) \rightarrow Zn^{2+}(aq) + H_2(g) \quad \text{(redox)}$$
$$Zn(s) \rightarrow Zn^{2+}(aq) + 2e \quad \text{(oxidation)}$$
$$2e + 2H^+(aq) \rightarrow H_2(g) \quad \text{(reduction)}$$

More complex cells

- Electricity can be produced in a cell by connecting two different metals in solutions of their ions.

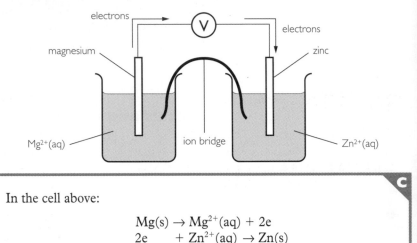

In the cell above:

$$Mg(s) \rightarrow Mg^{2+}(aq) + 2e$$
$$2e + Zn^{2+}(aq) \rightarrow Zn(s)$$

- All cells of this type must have an **ion bridge**, e.g. a piece of filter paper soaked in a salt solution. Its purpose is to complete the circuit.

Cells without metals

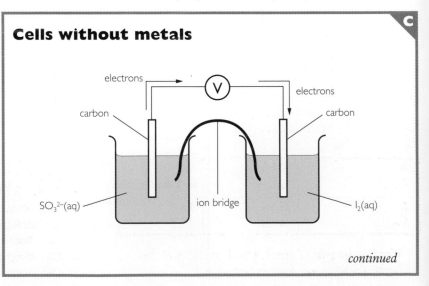

continued

C

- Carbon rods can be used to make contact with chemicals such as iodine and sulphite ions, which can also be used in a cell. In the cell at the bottom of the previous page:

$$SO_3^{2-}(aq) + H_2O(l) \rightarrow SO_4^{2-}(aq) + 2H^+(aq) + 2e$$
$$2e + I_2(aq) \rightarrow 2I^-(aq)$$

❖ Electrons flow in the external circuit (wires and meter) from the species higher in the ECS to the one lower down.

More about oxidation and reduction

- A metal element reacting to form a compound is considered to be an example of **oxidation**.
- A compound reacting to form a metal is considered to be an example of **reduction**.

QUESTIONS

1   Simple cells were set up as shown below by dipping different metals into a salt solution while they were connected by a voltmeter. The pairs of metals used are shown in the accompanying grid.

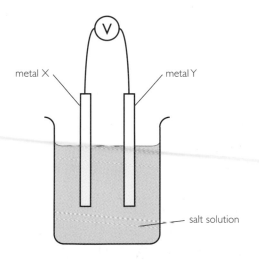

A	B	C
Al/Cu	Sn/Ni	Zn/Pb
D	**E**	**F**
Mg/Ag	Al/Zn	Mg/Fe

Identify the pair of metals which would give the highest reading on the voltmeter.

2   The diagram below shows two zinc/copper cells joined to produce a battery.

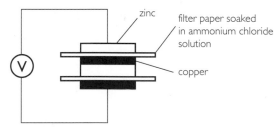

a) What direction would you expect the electrons to travel in through the wires and meter?
b) When the ammonium chloride solution is replaced by the liquid hydrocarbon octane (C_8H_{18}) what would you expect to happen to the reading on the voltmeter?
c) State what would happen to the meter reading if the copper was replaced by lead.

3   a) In some cases one metal can displace another. What is the general rule for the displacement of one metal by another?
    b) In which of the following cases will displacement take place:
        (i)   zinc + magnesium chloride solution
        (ii) aluminium + potassium sulphate solution
        (iii) magnesium + silver nitrate solution
        (iv) copper + sodium carbonate solution?

4 Give ion-electron equations, using state symbols, for any of the cases in question 3(b) where displacement took place. Add the words 'reduction' or 'oxidation' as appropriate. (The Electrochemical Series given in the data booklet may help with the ion-electron equations.)

5 Magnesium reacts rapidly with dilute sulphuric acid, displacing hydrogen gas.

a) Give the relevant ion-electron equations associated with this reaction, adding 'oxidation' and 'reduction' as appropriate.
b) Give the overall equation for the reaction as derived from the ion-electron equations (i.e. omitting spectator ions).

6 Apply the terms 'reduction', 'oxidation', 'redox' or 'none of these' to each of the following:

a) $F_2 + 2e \rightarrow 2F^-$
b) aluminium being formed from aluminium oxide
c) $2H^+(aq) + CO_3^{2-}(aq) \rightarrow H_2O(l) + CO_2(g)$
d) $SO_4^{2-} + 2H^+ + 2e \rightarrow SO_3^{2-} + H_2O$
e) $Fe^{2+}(aq) + Mg(s) \rightarrow Fe(s) + Mg^{2+}(aq)$
f) mercury reacting with iodine to form mercury(II) iodide
g) $4OH^- \rightarrow 2H_2O + O_2 + 4e$.

7 Miranda set up the cell shown below:

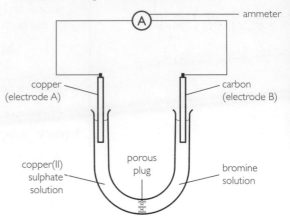

The reaction taking place at electrode B is:

$$Br_2(aq) + 2e \rightarrow 2Br^-(aq)$$

a) Name the type of reaction taking place at electrode B.
b) In which direction do electrons flow through the meter?
c) As the reaction proceeds the colour of the copper(II) sulphate solution changes in intensity.
   (i) Explain what is happening to cause this.
   (ii) Give the ion-electron equation for the reaction taking place at electrode A.

Metals

Physical properties and uses

- All metals conduct electricity when solid or liquid, e.g. copper and aluminium are used in electrical wiring and cables.
- All metals are shiny, e.g. aluminium is used as a mirror coating.
- All metals conduct heat well, e.g. iron and aluminium are used for saucepans, etc.
- All metals are malleable, i.e. they bend without breaking.
- Many metals are strong, e.g. titanium is used for aircraft engine parts.
- The specific properties of metals are related to their uses.
- The properties of metals can be changed by making alloys.

Alloys

- An **alloy** is a mixture of metals, or of metals and non-metals, melted together.
- Alloys are often harder and tougher than the original metals.
- Alloys can have much lower melting points than the original elements, e.g. solder, an alloy of tin and lead.
- Corrosion resistance can be improved by alloying, e.g. 'stainless' steel.
- Other alloys include bronze (copper/tin) and brass (copper/zinc).

Metals and recycling

- Metals should be recycled because they are finite resources and some are already in short supply.
- Recycling requires less energy than extracting fresh supplies of metals.

Chemical properties

- Metals can be placed in a **reactivity series** by observing their reactions. (See the first table on the following page).
- Potassium, sodium and lithium are stored in oil because they react quickly with oxygen and water in the air.
- These metals are also too reactive to risk in reactions with acids.
- Aluminium is slow to react with acids due to its thin protective coating of oxide.

Extracting metals

- Only unreactive metals like gold and silver occur uncombined in the Earth's crust.
- An **ore** is a naturally occurring compound of a metal from which the more reactive metals must be extracted.

- Many ores are oxides or can easily be converted to oxides from which the metal is extracted. (See the table at the bottom of this page).
- The higher a metal is in the reactivity series, the more stable are its compounds.
- Iron is extracted from iron ore in a **blast furnace**. A blast of air through hot carbon produces carbon monoxide, which reduces iron oxide to iron:

  iron oxide + carbon monoxide → iron + carbon dioxide

- Unreactive metals were among the first to be discovered because their extraction did not involve a chemical reaction.
- ❖ Social and industrial factors resulted in the large-scale extraction of more reactive metals, e.g. the demand for iron in the Industrial Revolution.

Metal	Reaction with		
	Oxygen	**Water**	**Dilute acid**
potassium		metal + water	metal
sodium		↓	+
lithium	metal	metal hydroxide	acid
calcium	+	+ hydrogen	↓
magnesium	oxygen		salt
aluminium	↓		+
zinc	metal oxide		hydrogen
iron			
tin			
lead			
copper			
mercury			
silver	no reaction	no reaction	no reaction
gold			

Metals can be placed in a reactivity series by observing their reactions.

Metal	Effect of heating metal oxide	
	Alone	**With carbon or carbon monoxide**
potassium		
sodium		
lithium		
calcium	no reaction	no reaction
magnesium		
aluminium		
zinc		metal oxide
iron		+
tin		carbon or carbon monoxide
lead		↓
copper		metal
mercury	metal oxide	+
silver	↓	carbon dioxide
gold	metal + oxygen	

Many ores are oxides from which the metal is extracted.

Reactivity and ease of metal extraction

- Reactive metals hold on to oxygen more strongly than less reactive metals.
- Heating alone is sufficient to release the metal from oxides of unreactive metals.
- Heating with carbon or carbon monoxide releases the metal from oxides of moderately reactive metals because carbon bonds more strongly with oxygen than the metal does.
- Heating with carbon does not release the metal from oxides of very reactive metals because the metal bonds more strongly with oxygen than carbon does.

Metal extraction and reduction

- The extraction of a metal from its ore is an example of **reduction** because the most important process taking place is gain of electrons by metal ions to form metal atoms.

QUESTIONS

A	B	C
Na_2O	ZnO	SnO_2
D	**E**	**F**
PbO	CuO	HgO

Identify the oxide which:

a) could be decomposed to the metal by heat alone
b) could *not* be decomposed to the metal by heating with carbon.

Titanium is used for some engine parts in Formula One racing cars. Suggest *two* properties of titanium which make it suitable for this purpose.

British coins are in fact alloys. A 20p coin contains copper (84%) and nickel (16%), a 50p coin contains copper (75%) and nickel (25%), and a £1 coin contains copper (70%), nickel (5.5%) and zinc (24.5%). Present this information in the form of a table.

4 Wood's metal is an alloy containing bismuth (50%), lead (25%), tin (12.5%) and cadmium (12.5%). It has a melting point of 70°C and is used in devices for fire prevention.

a) What is meant by the term 'an alloy'?
b) Draw a pie chart to show the composition of Wood's metal.
c) Explain how you think Wood's metal might be used in a fire prevention device.

5 Lithium is unusual in that it reacts quite rapidly with water while moving around on the water's surface. In the experiment shown below, universal indicator had been added to the water in the trough.

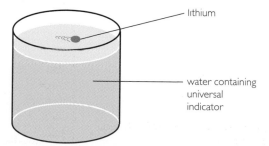

lithium

water containing universal indicator

a) Name *two* other metals which react with water in a similar way.

b) What colour change would you expect in the universal indicator as the reaction proceeded?

c) (i) Give a word equation for the reaction taking place.

(ii) Give an unbalanced chemical equation using symbols and simple formulae.

(iii) Give a balanced equation for the reaction, showing ions, where appropriate, and state symbols.

6 Give the same three types of equation as described in question 5(c) for the reactions between:

a) magnesium and oxygen
b) zinc and dilute sulphuric acid
c) aluminium and dilute hydrochloric acid.

7 It is possible to obtain zinc from zinc oxide by heating with carbon, but aluminium cannot be obtained from aluminium oxide in the same way. Explain why this is so.

8 Tin(II) oxide and copper(II) oxide can be converted to the metal by heating with carbon monoxide.

a) Write chemical equations for these processes using ionic formulae, where appropriate, and giving state symbols.

b) Explain which of the two oxides would be the easier to convert to the metal.

c) Explain whether the reactions should be categorised as either oxidation or reduction.

9 Hydrogen can be used in the extraction of metals from metal oxides. Where there is a reaction, hydrogen removes oxygen from the oxide to form water. Write a balanced equation for the reaction between lead(IV) oxide and hydrogen which takes place on heating.

Corrosion

- **Corrosion** is a chemical reaction that involves the surface of a metal changing from an element to a compound.
- More reactive metals corrode at a faster rate than less reactive metals.
- The term used to describe the corrosion of iron (or steel) is **rusting**.
- **Rust** is the name of the compound formed when iron corrodes.
- Both water and oxygen (from the air) are needed for iron to rust.
- The presence of dissolved salts speeds up rusting (they act as electrolytes).
- Salt (sodium chloride) spread on roads during winter speeds up the rusting of exposed iron and steel on cars, etc.

C

- Strictly speaking, water, oxygen and a dissolved electrolyte are needed for the rusting of iron. (Dissolved carbon dioxide can act as an electrolyte since it reacts with water, producing ions.)

- The first stage in the rusting of iron is that iron atoms lose two electrons each to form $Fe^{2+}(aq)$ ions.
- **Ferroxyl indicator** can be used to show when rusting is taking place because it forms a **blue** colour with $Fe^{2+}(aq)$ ions. The more blue colour produced, the greater is the amount of rusting that has occurred.

C

Rusting as a redox process

- The first stage of rusting is loss of electrons to form iron(II) ions:

$$Fe(s) \rightarrow Fe^{2+}(aq) + 2e \qquad \text{(oxidation)}$$

- In solution the iron(II) ions lose another electron to form iron(III) ions:

$$Fe^{2+}(aq) \rightarrow Fe^{3+}(aq) + e \qquad \text{(oxidation)}$$

- The electrons lost are gained by water and oxygen, forming hydroxide ions:

$$4e + 2H_2O(l) + O_2(aq) \rightarrow 4OH^-(aq) \qquad \text{(reduction)}$$

- Ferroxyl indicator turns **pink** in the presence of $OH^-(aq)$ ions.
- When $Fe^{3+}(aq)$ ions and $OH^-(aq)$ ions meet, rust forms. This can be looked upon as either iron(III) hydroxide or as a form of iron(III) oxide.

Acid rain and corrosion

Acid rain speeds up the rusting of iron because (a) it contains sulphuric and nitric acids which are electrolytes and (b) they react with iron: e.g. $Fe + H_2SO_4 \rightarrow FeSO_4 + H_2$. Both (a) and (b) speed up the formation of $Fe^{2+}(aq)$ ions.

Protection against corrosion

- Coating a metal with paint, oil, grease, plastic or another metal provides **physical protection** because contact with air and water is prevented.
- When a metal corrodes it loses electrons. This can be stopped by attaching the metal to the **negative** terminal of a battery or other d.c. supply. By doing this electrons flow to the metal, preventing corrosion.
- A metal higher in the ECS can provide **sacrificial protection** to one lower down. When in contact, or joined by a wire, electrons can flow from the higher metal to the lower one. The higher metal is sacrificed but the lower one is protected, e.g. magnesium is attached to iron pipes using wires and zinc is attached to the iron hulls of ships.

C

- Electrons flow away from iron when it rusts (see the iron/carbon cell shown below).
  At the iron:

$$Fe(s) \rightarrow Fe^{2+}(aq) + 2e$$

At the carbon:

$$4e + 2H_2O(l) + O_2(aq) \rightarrow 4OH^-(aq)$$

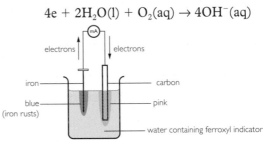

- In a magnesium/iron cell, electrons flow from magnesium, which is higher in the ECS, to the iron. At the magnesium:

$$Mg(s) \rightarrow Mg^{2+}(aq) + 2e$$

At the iron:

$$4e + 2H_2O(l) + O_2(aq) \rightarrow 4OH^-(aq)$$

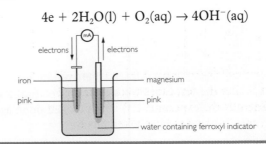

Galvanising iron

- Iron objects are dipped in molten zinc to give a coating of zinc metal.
- Galvanising provides physical protection, keeping out air and water.
- Galvanising can also provide sacrificial protection because even when the zinc coating is broken electrons can flow from the zinc (the metal higher in the ECS) to protect the iron.
- A variety of iron and steel objects can be galvanised, from nails to car bodies.

Tin-plated iron

- Tin provides only physical protection for iron.
- When the tin coating is broken, the iron rusts very rapidly. This is because iron is above tin in the ECS and electrons flow from the iron to the tin.

Electroplating

Electroplating is a process in which a layer of metal, such as zinc, nickel, silver, etc., is deposited on another metal by electrolysis. The object to be electroplated is used as the negative electrode in a solution containing ions of the metal being deposited.

QUESTIONS

1   Four experiments to study the rusting of iron nails were set up:

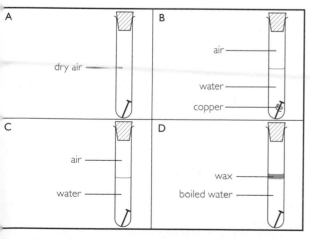

Two days later the test tubes were examined again. Identify the experiment(s) in which you would expect rusting to have taken place.

2

A	B	C
tin	zinc	nickel
D	**E**	**F**
lead	magnesium	gold

a) Identify the metal used to galvanise iron and steel.

b) Identify the metal(s) that could provide sacrificial protection for iron.

3   Silver tarnishes slowly in air with a dark brown layer forming on its surface.

a) What type of substance is the dark brown layer, assuming that it is formed as a result of silver corroding?

b) Give an example of a metal element which would be expected to corrode even more slowly than silver.

4 When iron rusts Fe^{2+}(aq) ions are formed initially.

   a) Name the reagent that is used to test for the presence of Fe^{2+}(aq).

   b) Describe the result of this test if Fe^{2+}(aq) ions are present.

5 A zinc coating on iron gives the iron physical protection while the coating is intact and chemical protection when the coating is broken.

   a) Explain what is meant by 'physical protection' in this context.

   b) Explain how the zinc coating can give chemical protection to the iron, even when the coating is broken.

   c) Give another name for the chemical protection provided by the zinc.

6 Alan, a garage mechanic, found that the aluminium body panels of a vehicle were badly pitted with corrosion close to where they were bolted onto the steel chassis, which was relatively rust-free. Explain why the aluminium would corrode in this way.

7 **C**

A	$4e + O_2 + 2H_2O \rightarrow 4OH^-$
B	$H_2 \rightarrow 2H^+ + 2e$
C	$Fe \rightarrow Fe^{2+} + 2e$
D	$3e + Fe^{3+} \rightarrow Fe$
E	$H^+ + OH^- \rightarrow H_2O$
F	$Fe^{3+} + e \rightarrow Fe^{2+}$

   a) Identify the reaction(s) that occur(s) during the rusting of iron.

   b) Identify the reaction that does *not* involve either oxidation or reduction.

8 Michelle set up the following experiment:

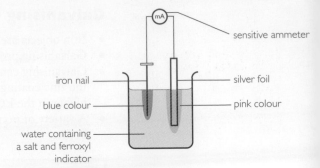

iron nail — silver foil
blue colour — pink colour
water containing a salt and ferroxyl indicator
sensitive ammeter
mA

   a) In which direction would electrons flow through the wires and meter?

   b) Give ion-electron equations for the reactions taking place at (i) the iron nail and (ii) the piece of silver foil, which would account for the colours produced.

9 The Statue of Liberty consists of 32.5 tonnes of beaten copper attached by flat iron bars to an inner iron framework.

   a) Explain the corrosion implications of this design.

   b) Suggest a means of attaching the copper figure to the iron framework, which would eliminate the corrosive effects described in (a).

10 James set up the following experiment as part of a rusting of iron project:

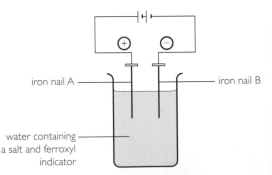

iron nail A — iron nail B
water containing a salt and ferroxyl indicator

   a) Which nail is protected from rusting in this experiment?

   b) Explain in terms of direction of electron flow why one nail in this experiment is protected but the other rusts rapidly.

   c) Give an everyday example of this method of corrosion protection.

Plastics

- **Plastics** and **synthetic fibres** are examples of **polymers** – very large molecules formed by the joining of many small molecules called **monomers**.
- **Monomers** are small molecules that can join together to form a large **polymer** molecule.
- **Polymerisation** is the process whereby many small monomer molecules join to form one large polymer molecule.
- Most plastics and synthetic fibres are made from molecules in crude oil.
- A **synthetic** fibre is one that is man-made, e.g. nylon and terylene.
- A **natural** fibre is one that is found in nature, e.g. wool, silk and cotton.

Synthetic and natural fibres compared

Advantages of natural fibres:
- Wool is warm and soft.
- Cotton is cool and is also soft.

Advantages of synthetic fibres:
- Water evaporates quickly from nylon and terylene.
- ❖ Nomex and Kevlar are very flame-resistant.

Synthetic and traditional materials compared

- Plastics are often used in place of traditional materials such as wood, paper, etc.
- The particular use is related to the properties of the plastic.
- Most have low density, are good heat and electrical insulators, and are water-resistant.
- PVC has replaced iron for pipes, etc. because it is durable and water-resistant.
- ❖ Kevlar has replaced wood in hockey sticks and other materials in tennis racquets because it is strong and flexible.

Plastics and pollution

- Most plastics are not **biodegradable** – they do not rot away naturally. They can therefore cause a long-term litter problem.
- The natural materials wood, paper and cardboard are biodegradable.
- Like all carbon-containing material plastics can give off poisonous carbon monoxide if combustion is incomplete.
- Some plastics can give off other toxic gases when they burn or smoulder.

- The gases given off during burning or smouldering can be related to elements in the plastic.

Gas produced	Elements present	Example of plastic
carbon monoxide, CO	C	polystyrene
hydrogen chloride, HCl	H and Cl	PVC
hydrogen cyanide, HCN	H, C and N	polyurethane

Thermoplastics and thermosetting plastics

- A **thermoplastic** plastic is one that softens on heating, e.g. polythene, perspex, etc.
- A **thermosetting** plastic does not soften on heating, e.g. bakelite, formica, etc.

Making polymers

- Many polymers are made from small unsaturated molecules produced by cracking.
- Some monomers are made from ethene, e.g. chloroethene (vinyl chloride).
- A polymer name is obtained by putting 'poly' in front of the monomer name.

Monomer	Polymer	Old name
ethene	poly(ethene)	polythene
propene	poly(propene)	polypropylene
chloroethene	poly(chloroethene)	polyvinyl chloride (PVC)

- During the polymerisation of ethene, many ethene monomers join to give one large poly(ethene) polymer:

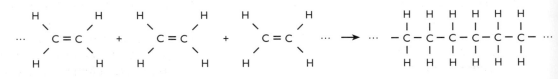

Addition polymerisation

- **Addition polymerisation** is a process in which many small monomer molecules join to form one large polymer molecule and nothing else, e.g. the formation of poly(ethene) from ethene.
- The monomers that undergo addition polymerisation all have a $C=C$ bond.

continued

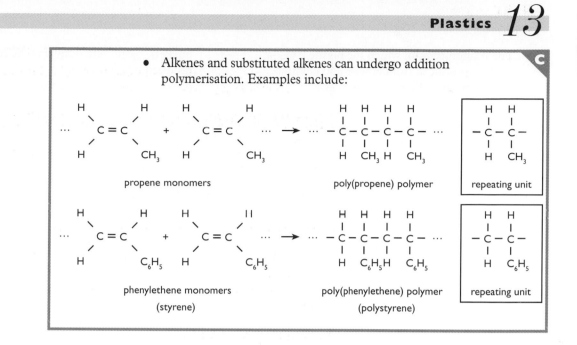

• Alkenes and substituted alkenes can undergo addition polymerisation. Examples include:

propene monomers → poly(propene) polymer → repeating unit

phenylethene monomers (styrene) → poly(phenylethene) polymer (polystyrene) → repeating unit

QUESTIONS

1 Some widely used fibres are shown in the grid below.

A	B	C
cotton	nylon (polyamide)	terylene (polyester)
D	E	F
poly(propene)	wool	silk

a) Identify the natural fibre that is obtained from a plant.
b) Identify the *two* natural fibres that are obtained from animals.
c) The remaining fibres in the grid are said to be 'synthetic'. What does the word 'synthetic' mean?

2 The four plastics that are produced in greatest quantity are shown in the table below. The figures given refer to a recent annual production survey.

Plastic	World production/million tonnes
PVC	16.5
polythene	16.0
poly(propene)	13.0
polystyrene	7.5

Give this information in the form of a bar graph.

3 Poly(propene) is one of the most versatile thermoplastic polymers commercially available. It can be fabricated into film, for packaging purposes, and into fibres, for carpets and clothing. It can also be injection-moulded for car bumpers, bowls, buckets, etc., and extruded into pipes.

a) What is meant by the term 'thermoplastic polymer'?
b) Why is poly(propene) described as 'versatile'?
c) One breakdown of the uses of poly(propene) gave the information in the table below. Present this information as a pie chart.

Use	% of total production
fibre	35
bumpers, bowls, etc.	25
film	20
packaging	10
other uses	10

4 The monomer from which the plastic PVC is made is produced from ethene and chlorine.

(i) Ethene and chlorine react to give 1,2-dichloroethane:

$$CH_2{=}CH_2 + Cl_2 \rightarrow CH_2Cl{-}CH_2Cl$$

(ii) The 1,2-dichloroethane is then heated strongly, decomposing it into chloroethene and hydrogen chloride.

Chloroethene, or vinyl chloride as it used to be called, is polymerised to give poly(chloroethene) or polyvinyl chloride (PVC). PVC can be made in a wide range of textures, from very flexible to very rigid. This can be done by mixing it with plasticisers, such as dibutyl phthalate, which act as lubricants for the polymer chains.

a) What *type* of reaction takes place between ethene and chlorine?

C

b) Give an equation, using full structural formulae, for the effect of heat on 1,2-dichloroethane.

---

c) What *type* of substance must PVC be mixed with in order to make it more flexible?

d) Explain how a substance like dibutyl phthalate can make PVC more flexible.

5 Plastic waste causes long-term litter problems in both town and country areas. Give two reasons for this.

6 Smouldering or burning plastics can produce toxic material in the form of smoke and gases. Polystyrene, for example, burns to give dense, sooty smoke due to its high carbon content.

a) What does the word 'toxic' mean?

b) Which toxic gas will all plastics produce if they burn in insufficient air for complete combustion to occur?

C

c) Which other toxic gas does PVC produce because of the chlorine it contains?

d) Which other toxic gas do polyurethanes produce because of the hydrogen, carbon and nitrogen they contain?

---

7 Some plastics can be blow-moulded to produce bottles, etc. or injection-moulded to produce buckets, basins, etc. Explain whether these production methods are consistent with the plastics concerned being thermoplastic or thermosetting.

8 Explain why a thermosetting plastic, usually melamine, is chosen as the surface for work-tops in a kitchen.

9 The monomer ethene can be polymerised to give the polymer poly(ethene).

a) Name the polymer produced from the monomer tetrafluoroethene.

b) Name the monomer used to produce the polymer poly(methyl-2-methyl-propenoate).

C

10 Teflon and Fluon are trade names for an addition polymer made by polymerising tetrafluoroethene. Plumbers use this polymer in the form of PTFE tape. The full structural formula of the monomer is:

a) Explain what is meant by the term 'addition polymer'.

b) Using full structural formulae, draw a representative part of the polymer molecule, showing at least three monomer molecules joined together.

c) Explain the reason for choosing the letters PTFE as the name for the plumber's special tape.

11 A new polymer has the following structure:

$$\cdots - \underset{\underset{H}{|}}{\overset{\overset{Cl}{|}}{C}} - \underset{\underset{CH_3}{|}}{\overset{\overset{H}{|}}{C}} - \underset{\underset{H}{|}}{\overset{\overset{Cl}{|}}{C}} - \underset{\underset{CH_3}{|}}{\overset{\overset{H}{|}}{C}} - \underset{\underset{H}{|}}{\overset{\overset{Cl}{|}}{C}} - \underset{\underset{CH_3}{|}}{\overset{\overset{H}{|}}{C}} - \cdots$$

a) Draw the full structural formula for the repeating unit in the polymer.

b) Draw the full structural formula for the monomer from which the polymer is made.

Fertilisers

- Increasing world population has led to a need for more efficient food production.
- Plants require **nutrients** (substances which help them to grow), including compounds of **nitrogen, phosphorus** and **potassium**.

C
- Farmers use a wide variety of **NPK** (nitrogen, phosphorus, potassium) fertilisers because different crops need fertilisers with different proportions of nitrogen, phosphorus and potassium.

- Crops remove nutrients from the soil.
- **Fertilisers** are substances which restore the elements essential for plant growth to the soil.
- **Nitrogen fixing bacteria** in root nodules of some plants (peas, beans, clover, etc.) can convert atmospheric nitrogen into nitrogen compounds that act as plant nutrients.

C
- Bacterial methods of fixing nitrogen (converting atmospheric nitrogen into nitrogen compounds) are cheaper than chemical methods carried out by farmers.

- **Natural fertilisers** include plant compost and animal manure. Both contain nitrogen compounds and are important in **recycling** nitrogen into the soil.
- **Synthetic fertilisers** are man-made. They include ammonia and ammonium salts, potassium salts, nitrates and phosphates. Compounds used as fertilisers must be **soluble** in water so that they can be absorbed by plants.
- Synthetic fertilisers can be washed into rivers, lochs, etc. where they cause pollution, e.g. harmful nitrate ions can make water unfit to drink and plants and algae can grow excessively.

The nitrogen cycle

- There are various ways in which nitrogen is recycled between animals and plants. These can be shown in a **nitrogen cycle** (see the figure on the following page).
- There are various ways in which nitrogen can be gained and lost in the nitrogen cycle.

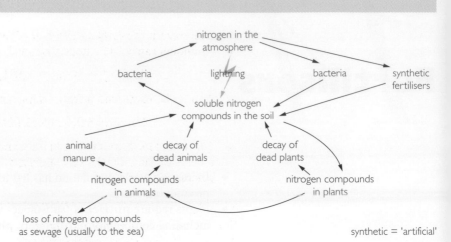

synthetic = 'artificial'

Ammonia

- **Ammonia** (NH_3) is used as a fertiliser and is used to make other fertilisers.
- Ammonia is manufactured by the **Haber process** in which nitrogen (obtained from the air) and hydrogen (obtained from methane in natural gas) are passed over an iron catalyst at moderately high temperature (about 500°C) and high pressure (about 200 atmospheres). Some ammonia is formed as the result of a reversible reaction:

$$N_2(g) + 3H_2(g) \rightleftharpoons 2NH_3(g)$$

The mixture is cooled so that the ammonia formed liquefies and can be run off. More nitrogen and hydrogen are added and the unreacted gases are recycled through the catalyst chamber.

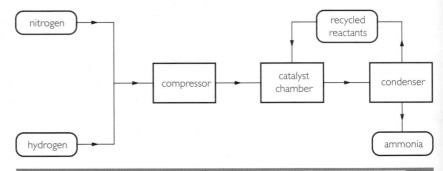

- The Haber process is carried out at **moderately** high temperatures because:
  - (a) the reaction is too **slow** at lower temperatures
  - (b) the percentage conversion is too **low** at higher temperatures.
- All the nitrogen and hydrogen are not converted to ammonia because the reaction is **reversible**.

- Ammonia is a colourless gas with a sharp, unpleasant smell.
- Ammonia is very soluble in water producing an **alkaline** solution:

$$NH_3(aq) + H_2O(l) \rightleftharpoons NH_4^+(aq) + OH^-(aq)$$

- Ammonia is the **only** common alkaline gas.
- Ammonia can act as a neutraliser with acids, accepting hydrogen ions:

$$NH_3(aq) + H^+(aq) \rightarrow NH_4^+(aq) \text{ (ammonium ion)}$$

- Ammonia reacts with acids forming ammonium salts, e.g.

$$2NH_3 + H_2SO_4 \rightarrow (NH_4)_2SO_4 \text{ (ammonium sulphate)}$$

- The fertilisers ammonium nitrate, ammonium sulphate and ammonium phosphate are made by reacting ammonia with nitric, sulphuric and phosphoric acids.

- Ammonia gas is given off when an **ammonium salt** is heated with an **alkali** such as sodium hydroxide. Ammonia is prepared in the laboratory using this reaction, e.g.

$$NH_4Cl + NaOH \rightarrow NaCl + H_2O + NH_3$$

Turning nitrogen into nitric acid

- Nitrogen is very unreactive because a lot of energy is needed to break the $N\equiv N$ bond.
- A spark (e.g. in a petrol engine) or lightning can provide the energy needed to break the $N\equiv N$ bond and cause a reaction with oxygen, producing acidic nitrogen dioxide gas.
- **Nitric acid** is formed when nitrogen dioxide, in the presence of air, dissolves in water.
- The combination of nitrogen and oxygen does not provide an economical industrial route to nitric acid.
- The economical route to nitric acid from nitrogen is first to make ammonia (by the Haber process) and then to oxidise the ammonia catalytically by the **Ostwald process**.
- In the Ostwald process, ammonia and air are passed through a platinum gauze catalyst at a moderately high temperature (about 800°C) at which ammonia and oxygen react to give nitrogen monoxide and steam.

- It is not necessary to supply heat once the catalytic oxidation of ammonia has started because the reaction is **exothermic**.
- The reasons for carrying out the reaction at a **moderately** high temperature are similar to those given above for the Haber process.

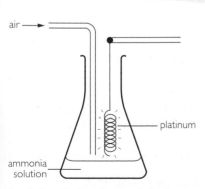

Catalytic oxidation of ammonia in the laboratory. Once heated, the platinum spiral continues to glow.

- The nitrogen monoxide produced combines readily with oxygen in the air to produce nitrogen dioxide.
- Nitric acid is formed when nitrogen dioxide, in the presence of air, dissolves in water.
- Nitric acid is used in the production of **nitrate** fertilisers, e.g. ammonium nitrate.

1 Gases are important reactants in some industrial processes. Some are shown in the grid below:

A	B	C
nitrogen dioxide	hydrogen	oxygen
D	**E**	**F**
carbon dioxide	ammonia	nitrogen

Identify:

a) the *two* gases used as reactants in the Haber process

b) the *two* gases used as reactants in the Ostwald process

c) the gas that is produced during lightning storms and near spark plugs inside car engines

d) the gas that makes up about 80% of the air

e) the gas that dissolves to give an alkaline solution

f) the gas that is produced by the Haber process.

2 Compounds of nitrogen, phosphorus and potassium are essential plant nutrients. Nitrogen is needed for root development and leaf growth. Potassium promotes the rate of growth. Phosphorus regulates leaf development and size.

a) Explain what is meant by the term 'nutrient'.

b) Present this information in the form of a table.

3 Ammonia gas can be produced using the apparatus shown below:

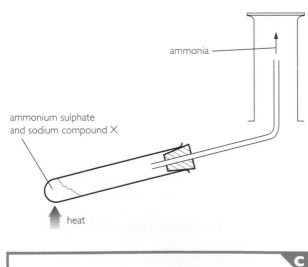

ammonia

ammonium sulphate and sodium compound X

heat

a) Name a suitable sodium compound X which could be used in the experiment.

b) What can be concluded regarding the density of ammonia based on the method of collection used?

c) Why is ammonia not collected over water?

d) Why should the experiment be carried out in a fume cupboard?

4 Mr Thomson told his class that he was going to make a 'chemical light'. He first poured some concentrated ammonia solution into a conical flask. The class could all smell the ammonia gas coming from it. Next, he heated a spiral of platinum wire in a Bunsen flame then, while it was still hot, he lowered it into the conical flask so that it was just above the concentrated ammonia solution. The platinum spiral, which had gone quite dull, became bright again and gave off a lot of light. It continued to glow brightly for the remaining fifteen minutes of the lesson.

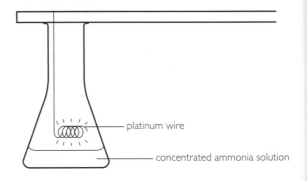

platinum wire

concentrated ammonia solution

a) Which two gases were reacting on the surface of the platinum wire?

b) What role did the platinum play in the reaction?

c) Why did the platinum wire continue to glow?

d) Give a balanced equation for the reaction taking place on the surface of the platinum wire.

5 Rain falling at the Glasgow Weather Centre was found to have a pH of 5.23, then a lightning storm started. At the height of the storm the pH of the rain falling had dropped to 4.17.

a) Explain how the lightning storm could have affected the pH of the rain-water.

b) Name the acid which is produced in rain-water during lightning storms.

6 Compost and manure are natural fertilisers, typically containing 0.5% nitrogen, 0.15% phosphorus and 0.4% potassium.

a) What is meant by the word 'fertiliser'?
b) Since natural fertilisers are available, why are artificial fertilisers used as well?

7 Potassium chloride, which is used as a source of potassium in some fertilisers, can be made by reacting potassium hydroxide with hydrochloric acid.

a) Give a balanced equation for this reaction.
b) Calculate the percentage by mass of potassium in potassium chloride, KCl.

8 Phosphoric acid, H_3PO_4, which is used in the production of phosphate fertilisers, is made by mixing calcium phosphate with sulphuric acid. The only other product of the reaction is calcium sulphate. Write a balanced chemical equation for the reaction.

9 Diammonium hydrogenphosphate is a major fertiliser made from ammonia and phosphoric acid:

$$2NH_3 + H_3PO_4 \rightarrow (NH_4)_2HPO_4$$

a) What mass of diammonium hydrogenphosphate fertiliser could be made by complete reaction of 1 kg of ammonia?
b) Calculate the percentage, by mass, of nitrogen and phosphorus in this fertiliser.

Carbohydrates

- Plants make carbohydrates (high energy foods for animals) from carbon dioxide and water during **photosynthesis**, releasing oxygen at the same time:

$$6CO_2 + 6H_2O \rightarrow C_6H_{12}O_6 (glucose) + 6O_2$$

- Photosynthesis takes place in the leaves of plants where the green compound **chlorophyll** absorbs the light energy needed for carbon dioxide and water to react.
- Plants and animals obtain energy (for warmth, movement and growth) on breaking down carbohydrates, by reaction with oxygen, during **respiration**, releasing carbon dioxide and water at the same time:

$$C_6H_{12}O_6 (glucose) + 6O_2 \rightarrow 6CO_2 + 6H_2O$$

- Photosynthesis and respiration are important in maintaining a **balance** of oxygen and carbon dioxide in the air.
- The extensive clearing of forests reduces the amount of photosynthesis taking place.
- The burning of plant material and fossil fuels takes oxygen from the air, replacing it with carbon dioxide.
- The amount of carbon dioxide in the air is rising and, since it traps heat near the surface of the earth ('greenhouse' effect), this could lead to global warming.
- All carbohydrates burn producing carbon dioxide and water:

carbohydrate + oxygen → carbon dioxide + water

- The production of carbon dioxide and water, on burning, indicates the presence of **carbon** and **hydrogen** in the carbohydrate.

- All carbohydrates are **covalent** compounds containing the elements **carbon**, **hydrogen** and **oxygen**, with two hydrogen atoms for every one oxygen atom.

Carbohydrates large and small

- **Sugars** are sweet-tasting, water-soluble carbohydrates made of fairly small molecules, e.g. glucose, fructose, sucrose and maltose.

- **Starch** and **cellulose** are made of large, insoluble polymer molecules with no sweet taste.
- When a beam of light is passed through a sugar solution, the path is not seen because sugar molecules are too small to reflect light.
- When a beam of light is passed through a dispersion of starch in water (starch 'solution'), the path is visible because starch molecules are large enough to reflect light.

- Glucose and fructose are **monosaccharides** with molecular formula $C_6H_{12}O_6$.
- Maltose and sucrose are **disaccharides** with molecular formula $C_{12}H_{22}O_{11}$.
- Starch and cellulose are **polysaccharides** with molecular formula $(C_6H_{10}O_5)_n$.

- In plants, glucose (a monomer) is **polymerised** to form starch (a polymer).

- The joining of glucose monomers to form a starch polymer is an example of **condensation polymerisation** since water is formed at the same time:

$$nC_6H_{12}O_6 \rightarrow (C_6H_{10}O_5)_n + nH_2O$$

Breaking down carbohydrates

- During **digestion** starch is broken down into glucose.
- Glucose can pass through the gut wall but starch cannot.
- **Enzymes** act as biological catalysts in the breakdown of complex food molecules.
- In the body, the enzyme **amylase** catalyses the breakdown of starch to glucose.

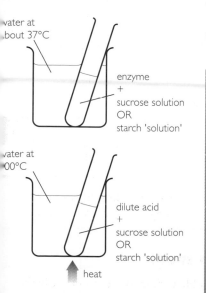

water at about 37°C

enzyme + sucrose solution OR starch 'solution'

water at 100°C

dilute acid + sucrose solution OR starch 'solution'

heat

Two ways of hydrolysing starch or sucrose

- The breakdown of large carbohydrates into simpler ones is an example of **hydrolysis**.
- A **hydrolysis** reaction is one in which a large molecule is broken down into two or more smaller molecules by reaction with water.
- Starch can be hydrolysed rapidly using amylase at about body temperature (37°C) or more slowly using dilute acid at 100°C:

$$(C_6H_{10}O_5)_n + nH_2O \rightarrow nC_6H_{12}O_6$$

- Sucrose can also be hydrolysed rapidly using an enzyme at about 37°C or more slowly using dilute acid at 100°C:

$$C_{12}H_{22}O_{11} + H_2O \rightarrow C_6H_{12}O_6 + C_6H_{12}O_6$$
$$\text{glucose} \qquad \text{fructose}$$

continued

- The progress of the above reactions may be followed by testing samples at intervals with Benedict's (or Fehling's) solution. (Tests are given on page 90.)
- The hydrolysis products may be identified using **chromatography**.

Alcoholic drinks

- Alcohol can be made from any fruit or vegetable containing starch or sugars, e.g. grapes contain glucose, barley contains starch, etc.
- The alcohol in alcoholic drinks is **ethanol**, the second member of a chemical family of compounds called the **alkanols**.
- If starch is used, it must first be broken down to glucose using enzymes.
- Alcohol (ethanol) is obtained from glucose by a process of **fermentation**.
- **Fermentation** is the breakdown of glucose to form alcohol (ethanol) and carbon dioxide. An enzyme in **yeast**, a living organism, acts as a catalyst for the reaction:

glucose → ethanol + carbon dioxide

$$C_6H_{12}O_6 \rightarrow 2C_2H_5OH + 2CO_2$$

- There is a limit to the alcohol concentration of fermented drinks because yeast cells die if the concentration rises above about 12%.
- Like all enzymes, those used in fermentation have a pH and a temperature at which they work best (their **optimum** pH and temperature).

The effect of temperature on an enzyme-catalysed reaction

- Because water boils at 100°C and ethanol boils at 78°C, the two can be separated by **distillation**. This enables high alcohol content drinks such as whisky, to be produced.
- Typical alcohol contents: beer/lager 3–7%; wine 10–12%; spirits 40%.

QUESTIONS

1

A	B	C
nitrogen	oxygen	water
D	**E**	**F**
carbon dioxide	methane	ethanol

Identify:

a) the substance(s) used by plants during photosynthesis

b) the *two* substances produced during fermentation of glucose solution

c) the substance(s) produced during respiration in humans

d) the substance used up during combustion of starch.

2 Some important carbohydrates are shown in the grid:

A	B	C
cellulose	sucrose	maltose
D	**E**	**F**
glucose	starch	fructose

Identify:

a) the substance(s) that gives a dark blue colour with iodine solution

b) the *sugar* that does *not* give a positive result with Benedict's solution

c) the substances that are isomers with molecular formula $C_6H_{12}O_6$

d) the substances that are isomers with molecular formula $C_{12}H_{22}O_{11}$.

3 A compound Z, thought to be a carbohydrate, was burned and found to produce a colourless liquid X and carbon dioxide.

a) What two tests could be carried out to prove that the colourless liquid X was pure water?

b) What test could be carried out to prove that carbon dioxide had been formed?

c) What conclusions can be reached regarding the elements present in the compound Z based on the information that water and carbon dioxide are formed when it burns?

4 The experiment shown in the diagram below was set up to obtain information about the relative sizes of glucose and starch molecules.

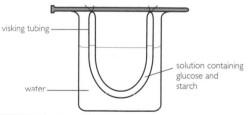

visking tubing

solution containing glucose and starch

water

Visking tubing is porous and behaves like the gut wall. After about half an hour, tests were carried out on the liquids inside the visking tubing and in the beaker.

Test	Iodine solution	Benedict's solution
liquid inside tubing	dark blue colour produced	orange–red colour produced on heating
liquid in beaker	no colour change	orange–red colour produced on heating

a) Explain why the liquid in the beaker gave a positive result with Benedict's solution, but not with iodine solution.

b) What can be concluded about the relative sizes of glucose and starch molecules?

5 Cellulose is a *polymer* made by a process of *condensation polymerisation* from the *monomer* glucose.

a) Explain the meaning of the following terms:
(i) monomer
(ii) polymer
(iii) condensation polymerisation.

b) Name another polymer that is made by glucose molecules joining together.

6 A solution of maltose was *hydrolysed* by warming it with an *enzyme* at its *optimum temperature* of 37°C. A sample of the hydrolysed mixture was subjected to chromatography, along with standard solutions of glucose, fructose and maltose. The following chromatogram was obtained:

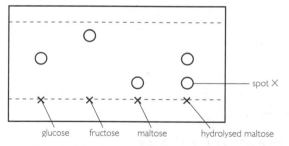

spot X

glucose   fructose   maltose   hydrolysed maltose

a) Explain the meaning of the following terms:
(i) hydrolysis
(ii) enzyme
(iii) optimum temperature

b) Name another variable that can affect the activity of an enzyme.

c) Based on the results of this experiment, identify the product(s) of the hydrolysis of maltose and give a balanced chemical equation for the reaction.

d) Explain the significance of spot X on the chromatogram.

part 2 Formulae, Equations & Calculations etc: Examples & Questions

Simple formulae for compounds I

Simple formulae for two-element compounds

- The simplest formulae for compounds, both covalent and ionic, indicate the ratio of atoms present.
- In the case of covalent compounds that exist as molecules, the simplest formula is often the molecular formula, e.g. H_2O.
- Simple formulae for compounds can be worked out using the system of **valency numbers**.
- The **valency** of an element is its combining power. The valencies of main group elements in the periodic table are as follows:

Group number	1	2	3	4	5	6	7	0
Valency	1	2	3	4	3	2	1	0

- By following a step-by-step process the simple formula for any compound formed between two main group elements can be found.

Example 1

Work out the simple formula for carbon sulphide.

Step 1	symbols	C S
Step 2	valencies	4 2 (carbon is in Group 4, sulphur is in Group 6)
Step 3	cross over valencies	C_2S_4
Step 4	cancel out any common factor	C_1S_2
Step 5	omit '1' if present	CS_2

The simple formula for carbon sulphide is CS_2.

Compound formulae from prefixes

- The ratio of atoms present in a molecule can be indicated by prefixes.
- If no prefix is given then it should be assumed that only one atom of that element is present in the formula.

Example 2

Nitrogen monoxide (mono = 1)
The simple formula is NO.

Example 3

Boron trichloride (tri = 3)
The simple formula is BCl_3.

Example 4

Silicon tetrachloride (tetra = 4)
The simple formula is $SiCl_4$.

- In examples 2, 3 and 4 above, the simple formula is also the molecular formula. Prefixes can also be used to give a molecular formula which is not the same as the simple formula.

Example 5

Dinitrogen tetraoxide (di = 2, tetra = 4)
The molecular formula is N_2O_4.

Note: penta = 5 and hexa = 6

Simple formulae for compounds containing complicated ions

- Complicated ions contain more than one kind of atom, e.g. NH_4^+, CO_3^{2-}. (The data booklet contains a table of ions which have more than one kind of atom in them.)
- The valency of ions is the same as the number of charges they have, e.g. the ammonium ion, NH_4^+, with one positive charge, has a valency of 1 and the carbonate ion, CO_3^{2-}, with two negative charges, has a valency of 2.
- Simple formulae for compounds containing complicated ions can be worked out using the valency number method.

Example 1

Work out the simple formula for ammonium chloride.

Step 1	symbols	NH_4 Cl	
Step 2	valencies	1 1	(chlorine is in
Step 3	cross over valencies	$(NH_4)_1Cl_1$	Group 7)
Step 4	cancel out any common factor	$(NH_4)_1Cl_1$	
Step 5	omit '1' if present	NH_4Cl	

The simple formula for ammonium chloride is NH_4Cl.

Example 2

Work out the simple formula for sodium carbonate.

Step 1	symbols	Na	CO_3
Step 2	valencies	1, 2	(sodium is in
Step 3	cross over valencies	$Na_2(CO_3)_1$	Group 1, $CO_3{}^{2-}$
Step 4	cancel out any common factor	$Na_2(CO_3)_1$	has two negative
Step 5	omit '1' if present	Na_2CO_3	charges)

The simple formula for sodium carbonate is Na_2CO_3.

QUESTIONS

1 The following compounds are made up of only two elements, both of which are in one of the main groups of the periodic table. Where hydrogen appears in a compound you should assume that it has a valency of one. Write simple chemical formulae for:

a) lithium oxide
b) magnesium iodide
c) hydrogen sulphide
d) aluminium chloride
e) potassium nitride
f) tin oxide
g) phosphorus bromide
h) beryllium sulphide
i) boron nitride
j) calcium phosphide
k) sodium fluoride
l) hydrogen fluoride
m) carbon bromide
n) magnesium nitride
o) phosphorus hydride
p) silicon oxide
q) calcium oxide
r) boron sulphide
s) aluminium oxide
t) nitrogen hydride
u) sodium bromide
v) calcium hydride

2 Make use of the prefixes in the following compounds to help you write formulae for them:

a) sulphur monochloride
b) germanium tetrachloride
c) carbon monoxide
d) dinitrogen oxide
e) diphosphorus trioxide
f) chlorine dioxide

3 Not every compound has a formula that can be predicted by the valency number method. Which of the compounds referred to in question 2 have formulae that disobey the rules of the valency number method?

4 In the series of compounds given below at least one of the ions present contains more than one kind of atom. You will not need any brackets in your final answer. Write simple chemical formulae for:

a) lithium sulphate
b) sodium hydrogencarbonate
c) ammonium bromide
d) potassium phosphate
e) rubidium nitrate
f) ammonium iodide
g) magnesium carbonate
h) potassium hydrogensulphite
i) lithium hydroxide
j) ammonium nitrate
k) calcium sulphate
l) aluminium phosphate
m) sodium hydrogensulphate
n) potassium hydroxide
o) sodium permanganate
p) magnesium sulphite
q) barium chromate
r) strontium carbonate
s) potassium dichromate
t) lithium phosphate
u) sodium sulphate
v) potassium hydrogencarbonate
w) ammonium hydrogensulphate
x) ammonium nitrite

Simple formulae for compounds II

Some Roman numbers used in chemistry
I = 1
II = 2
III = 3
IV = 4
V = 5
VI = 6
VII = 7

- Some metals may have more than one valency, e.g. iron can have a valency of two or three.
- Chemists use Roman numbers to indicate the valency of a metal where this might be in doubt, e.g. in the compound iron(III) oxide, the valency of iron is three.

Example 1

Work out the simple formula for iron(III) oxide.

Step 1	symbols	Fe O
Step 2	valencies	3 2
Step 3	cross over valencies	Fe_2O_3
Step 4	cancel out any common factor	Fe_2O_3
Step 5	omit '1' if present	Fe_2O_3

The simple formula for iron(III) oxide is Fe_2O_3.

- If more than one of the same complicated ion is present in a formula, then brackets must be used.

Example 2

In the compound calcium hydroxide there are two hydroxide ions for every one calcium ion and the simple formula is written as $Ca(OH)_2$. This formula may be worked out as follows:

Step 1	symbols	Ca OH
Step 2	valencies	2 1
Step 3	cross over valencies	$Ca_1(OH)_2$
Step 4	cancel out any common factor	$Ca_1(OH)_2$
Step 5	omit '1' if present	$Ca(OH)_2$

The simple formula for calcium hydroxide is $Ca(OH)_2$.

QUESTIONS

Simple formulae for compounds II

1 The following compounds contain only two elements. One is a metal with the valency shown by a Roman number, the other is a non-metal. Write simple chemical formulae for:

a) copper(I) chloride
b) copper(II) sulphide
c) copper(I) oxide
d) iron(II) chloride
e) iron(III) fluoride
f) manganese(II) oxide
g) manganese(IV) oxide
h) manganese(VI) oxide
i) manganese(VII) oxide
j) chromium(III) chloride
k) chromium(III) oxide
l) nickel(II) sulphide
m) nickel(III) oxide
n) chromium(VI) oxide
o) vanadium(V) oxide
p) uranium(VI) fluoride
q) tin(II) chloride
r) tin(IV) iodide
s) lead(II) sulphide
t) lead(IV) chloride

2 In the following series of compounds each has at least one ion that contains more than one kind of atom. You will need brackets in your answer. Write simple chemical formulae for:

a) calcium nitrate
b) barium hydrogencarbonate
c) ammonium sulphate
d) strontium hydrogensulphite
e) ammonium carbonate
f) ammonium phosphate
g) aluminium hydroxide
h) magnesium nitrate
i) magnesium hydrogensulphate
j) barium hydroxide
k) ammonium dichromate
l) calcium permanganate
m) magnesium phosphate
n) ammonium sulphite
o) calcium hydrogencarbonate
p) aluminium nitrate

3 In these compounds you require knowledge of the use of Roman numbers and/or the use of brackets. Write simple chemical formulae for:

a) copper(II) chromate
b) lead(II) nitrate
c) barium permanganate
d) silver(I) hydroxide
e) copper(II) sulphate
f) tin(II) hydroxide
g) chromium(III) sulphate
h) iron(III) nitrate
i) magnesium hydrogensulphite
j) silver(I) nitrate
k) cobalt(III) hydroxide
l) iron(III) phosphate
m) silver(I) carbonate
n) mercury(II) nitrate
o) tin(II) carbonate
p) gold(III) chloride

Chemical equations

- In all chemical reactions one or more new substances are formed. The initial substances are called the **reactants** and those formed are called the **products**.
- **Word equations** can be written for reactions, e.g.

  methane + oxygen → carbon dioxide + water

- In the word equation '+' means 'and' and '→' means 'react to produce'.
- Any word equation can be re-written using symbols and formulae for the reactants and products. For a **diatomic element**, the **molecular formula** is used, e.g. O_2 for oxygen, H_2 for hydrogen, etc. For all other elements, a single symbol is used, e.g. C for carbon, Zn for zinc, etc.

H_2		

N_2	O_2	F_2
		Cl_2
		Br_2
		I_2
		At_2

The diatomic elements

Example I

Sodium reacts with water to give sodium hydroxide and hydrogen.
Word equation:

  sodium + water → sodium hydroxide + hydrogen

Equation using symbols and formulae:

$$Na + H_2O \rightarrow NaOH + H_2$$

Example 2

When hydrogen burns, it combines with oxygen to produce water.
Word equation:

  hydrogen + oxygen → water

Equation using symbols and formulae:

$$H_2 + O_2 \rightarrow H_2O$$

QUESTIONS

1 When a substance burns in air it reacts with oxygen to form new substances called oxides (in most cases). Use this information to write word equations for the following:

a) magnesium burning to form magnesium oxide
b) carbon monoxide burning to form carbon dioxide
c) methane (CH_4) burning to form carbon dioxide and water
d) hydrogen sulphide burning to form water and sulphur dioxide.

2 Write equations using symbols and chemical
formulae for each of the following word equations:

    a) sodium + chlorine $\rightarrow$ sodium chloride
    b) magnesium + fluorine $\rightarrow$ magnesium fluoride
    c) aluminium + iodine $\rightarrow$ aluminium iodide
    d) carbon + oxygen $\rightarrow$ carbon dioxide
    e) lithium + water $\rightarrow$ lithium hydroxide +
                       hydrogen

3 Write equations using symbols and chemical
formulae for each of the following sentence
descriptions:

    a) when hot lithium is placed in bromine vapour
        the two elements react to produce lithium
        bromide
    b) when sodium is heated in a Bunsen flame it
        bursts into flames, combining with oxygen to
        form sodium oxide
    c) hydrogen and chlorine combine explosively in
        bright light to produce hydrogen chloride
    d) silicon hydride burns spontaneously in air to
        produce silicon dioxide and water
    e) calcium reacts quickly with water to produce
        calcium hydroxide and hydrogen.

Balancing chemical equations

- A **balanced chemical equation** is needed in order to carry out calculations, e.g. to predict the mass of a product in a reaction.
- A chemical equation is said to be **balanced** when there are equal numbers of each type of atom on both sides of the equation. This is logical since during chemical reactions atoms are not made or destroyed. In a chemical reaction all of the atoms which were present in the reactants are still present in the products.
- Equations should only be balanced by putting numbers **in front of** formulae. Formulae must not be altered in any way when balancing equations.
- It is usually advisable to start with the first element, starting from the left, and then to continue methodically through the equation. Make sure that you have not unbalanced any elements by making a final check.

Example 1

In the complete combustion of methane, methane and oxygen react to produce carbon dioxide and water. The word equation for this reaction is:

$$\text{methane} + \text{oxygen} \rightarrow \text{carbon dioxide} + \text{water}$$

Writing formulae in place of the names of the reactants and products gives the **unbalanced** chemical equation:

$$CH_4 + O_2 \rightarrow CO_2 + H_2O$$

Although there is one carbon atom on both sides of the equation, there are four hydrogen atoms on the left, but only two on the right. There are also two oxygen atoms on the left, but three on the right. This can be seen more clearly if full structural formulae are used:

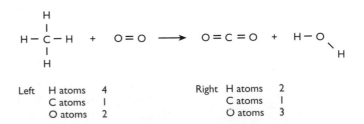

Left	H atoms	4
	C atoms	1
	O atoms	2

Right	H atoms	2
	C atoms	1
	O atoms	3

The four hydrogen atoms in the methane molecule will produce two water molecules, each containing two hydrogen atoms. Two oxygen molecules will be required to provide the four oxygen atoms that are present in the products:

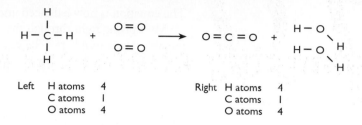

Left			Right		
	H atoms	4		H atoms	4
	C atoms	1		C atoms	1
	O atoms	4		O atoms	4

The balanced chemical equation can now be written as:

$$CH_4 + 2O_2 \rightarrow CO_2 + 2H_2O$$

Example 2

Balance the equation:

$$H_2 + O_2 \rightarrow H_2O$$

The hydrogen atoms are balanced in this case (two atoms on each side), so proceed to oxygen. There are two oxygen atoms on the left, but only one on the right, so we must put a 2 in front of H_2O. This gives:

$$H_2 + O_2 \rightarrow 2H_2O$$

However, checking through again, we find that there are two hydrogen atoms on the left, but four on the right. In order to have four hydrogen atoms on the left, we put a 2 in front of H_2. This gives:

$$2H_2 + O_2 \rightarrow 2H_2O$$

A final check shows that the equation is now balanced:

Left:	H atoms	4	Right:	H atoms	4
	O atoms	2		O atoms	2

• Sometimes the use of a fraction, such as $\frac{1}{2}$, can help balance an equation.

Example 3

Balance the equation:

$$C_2H_6 + O_2 \rightarrow CO_2 + H_2O$$

Balancing carbon atoms gives:

$$C_2H_6 + O_2 \rightarrow 2CO_2 + H_2O$$

Balancing hydrogen atoms gives:

$$C_2H_6 + O_2 \rightarrow 2CO_2 + 3H_2O$$

There are now seven oxygen atoms on the right so the number put in front of O_2 must give seven when multiplied by the 2 in O_2. This number is $3\frac{1}{2}$. This gives:

$$C_2H_6 + 3\tfrac{1}{2}O_2 \rightarrow 2CO_2 + 3H_2O$$

Left:	H atoms	6	Right:	H atoms	6
	C atoms	2		C atoms	2
	O atoms	7		O atoms	7

The equation is now balanced and is quite acceptable.

Multiplying right through the equation by two gives the simplest possible whole numbers. The equation then becomes:

$$2C_2H_6 + 7O_2 \rightarrow 4CO_2 + 6H_2O$$

Left:	H atoms	12	Right:	H atoms	12
	C atoms	4		C atoms	4
	O atoms	14		O atoms	14

- There are rare occasions when the methodical approach described in examples 2 and 3 does not lead to a balanced equation. In such cases a 'trial and error' method may be adopted, or it may be possible to solve the problem by a closer examination of the particular equation.

Example 4

Consider the balancing of the equation:

$$Fe_2O_3 + CO \rightarrow Fe + CO_2$$

Balancing the iron atoms gives:

$$Fe_2O_3 + CO \rightarrow 2Fe + CO_2$$

Trying to balance the carbon and oxygen atoms appears to be impossible by the usual method. However, it should be noticed that each carbon monoxide molecule removes one oxygen atom from the iron(III) oxide. There are three oxygen atoms to be removed and this therefore requires three carbon monoxide molecules. In turn, this leads to the production of three carbon dioxide molecules. The balanced equation is therefore:

$$Fe_2O_3 + 3CO \rightarrow 2Fe + 3CO_2$$

Left:	Fe atoms	2	Right:	Fe atoms	2
	O atoms	6		O atoms	6
	C atoms	3		C atoms	3

QUESTIONS

Balance the following equations. In each case give the simplest possible *whole numbers* in your final answer. Some equations are already balanced.

1 $Li + Cl_2 \rightarrow LiCl$

2 $H_2 + I_2 \rightarrow HI$

3 $Ca + O_2 \rightarrow CaO$

4 $N_2 + O_2 \rightarrow NO$

5 $Fe + HCl \rightarrow FeCl_2 + H_2$

6 $Mg + H_2SO_4 \rightarrow MgSO_4 + H_2$

7 $Al + HCl \rightarrow AlCl_3 + H_2$

8 $NaOH + H_2SO_4 \rightarrow Na_2SO_4 + H_2O$

9 $Ca(OH)_2 + HCl \rightarrow CaCl_2 + H_2O$

10 $Ba(OH)_2 + HNO_3 \rightarrow Ba(NO_3)_2 + H_2O$

11 $Sr(OH)_2 + H_2SO_4 \rightarrow SrSO_4 + H_2O$

12 $NH_3 + HCl \rightarrow NH_4Cl$

13    $NH_3 + H_2SO_4 \rightarrow (NH_4)_2SO_4$

14    $NH_3 + H_3PO_4 \rightarrow (NH_4)_3PO_4$

15    $NH_3 + O_2 \rightarrow N_2 + H_2O$

16    $Fe_2O_3 + H_2 \rightarrow Fe + H_2O$

17    $PbO_2 + CO \rightarrow Pb + CO_2$

18    $Al + Fe_2O_3 \rightarrow Fe + Al_2O_3$

19    $Fe_3O_4 + C \rightarrow Fe + CO_2$

20    $H_2O + CO \rightarrow H_2 + CO_2$

21    $NH_3 + O_2 \rightarrow NO + H_2O$

22    $FeS_2 + O_2 \rightarrow Fe_2O_3 + SO_2$

23    $MgCO_3 + HCl \rightarrow MgCl_2 + H_2O + CO_2$

24    $Na_2CO_3 + HNO_3 \rightarrow NaNO_3 + H_2O + CO_2$

25    $C_3H_8 + O_2 \rightarrow CO_2 + H_2O$

26    $C_2H_4 + O_2 \rightarrow CO_2 + H_2O$

27    $C_4H_{10} + O_2 \rightarrow CO_2 + H_2O$

28    $C_5H_{12} + O_2 \rightarrow CO_2 + H_2O$

29    $Ag_2CO_3 \rightarrow Ag + CO_2 + O_2$

30    $ZnCO_3 \rightarrow ZnO + CO_2$

31    $Mg + HNO_3 \rightarrow Mg(NO_3)_2 + H_2$

32    $(NH_4)_2Cr_2O_7 \rightarrow Cr_2O_3 + N_2 + H_2O$

33    $Na + H_2O \rightarrow NaOH + H_2$

34    $Ca + H_2O \rightarrow Ca(OH)_2 + H_2$

35    $Al + H_2SO_4 \rightarrow Al_2(SO_4)_3 + H_2$

36    $KNO_3 \rightarrow KNO_2 + O_2$

37    $HNO_3 \rightarrow H_2O + NO_2 + O_2$

38    $C_3H_6 + H_2O \rightarrow C_3H_8O$

39    $LiOH + H_3PO_4 \rightarrow Li_3PO_4 + H_2O$

40    $NaHCO_3 \rightarrow Na_2CO_3 + H_2O + CO_2$

41    $Al + Br_2 \rightarrow AlBr_3$

42    $K_2CO_3 + H_2SO_4 \rightarrow K_2SO_4 + H_2O + CO_2$

43    $Cu(NO_3)_2 \rightarrow CuO + NO_2 + O_2$

44    $AgNO_3 \rightarrow Ag + NO_2 + O_2$

45    $CO_2 + H_2O \rightarrow C_6H_{12}O_6 + O_2$

46    $C_6H_{12}O_6 \rightarrow C_2H_5OH + CO_2$

Ionic formulae for compounds

- A compound should be assumed to be ionic if it contains a metal or if it is an ammonium compound.
- When forming an ionic compound metals in Groups 1, 2 or 3 lose their outer electrons. By doing this they obtain the stable electron arrangement of a noble gas and form positively charged ions.
- When forming an ionic compound non-metals in Groups 5, 6 and 7 gain electrons to obtain the stable electron arrangement of a noble gas. By doing this they form negatively charged ions.
- In Group 4, the non-metals carbon and silicon do not form ions based on single atoms. In the same group, the metals tin and lead show variable valencies.
- The charges on ions of main group elements may be summarised as follows:

Group number	1	2	3	4	5	6	7	0
Charge on ion	1+	2+	3+	—	3−	2−	1−	—

Example 1

The ionic formula for calcium fluoride, which contains two main group elements, may be worked out as follows:

Step 1	symbols	Ca	F
Step 2	ions	Ca^{2+}	F^-
Step 3	number of ions to balance charges	$1Ca^{2+}$	$2F^-$ (2+ balances 2−)
Step 4	ionic formulae	$Ca^{2+}(F^-)_2$	

Note: Whereas in the simple formula, CaF_2, no brackets are required, they are required in the ionic formula. Brackets are always needed where more than one ion of a particular type is present in an ionic formula.

- Where a metal's valency is shown by a Roman number, this also gives the charge on the metal ion, e.g. any iron(II) compound will contain the ion Fe^{2+} and any copper(I) compound will contain the ion Cu^+.
- In the case of ions containing more than one element, the formula of the ion is given in the data booklet.

Example 2

The ionic formula of chromium(III) sulphite may be worked out as follows:

Step 1	ions	Cr^{3+}	SO_3^{2-}
Step 2	number of ions to balance charges	$2Cr^{3+}$	$3SO_3^{2-}$ (6+ balances 6−)
Step 3	ionic formula	$(Cr^{3+})_2(SO_3^{2-})_3$	

QUESTIONS

1 The following compounds are made up of two main group elements. Write ionic formulae for:

a) lithium oxide
b) magnesium iodide
c) aluminium fluoride
d) potassium nitride
e) calcium sulphide
f) sodium bromide
g) calcium phosphide
h) magnesium nitride
i) calcium oxide
j) aluminium oxide
k) rubidium chloride
l) strontium bromide

2 In the following compounds at least one of the ions contains more than one kind of atom but no brackets are needed. Write ionic formulae for:

a) lithium nitrate
b) sodium hydrogencarbonate
c) ammonium chloride
d) magnesium carbonate
e) calcium sulphate
f) potassium hydroxide
g) potassium permanganate
h) magnesium sulphite
i) barium chromate
j) ammonium nitrate
k) potassium hydrogensulphate
l) calcium dichromate

3 In the following compounds at least one of the ions contains more than one kind of atom. Brackets are needed in each case. Write ionic formulae for:

a) potassium phosphate
b) aluminium sulphate
c) lithium carbonate
d) calcium nitrate
e) barium hydrogencarbonate
f) ammonium sulphate
g) ammonium phosphate
h) aluminium hydroxide
i) magnesium hydrogensulphate
j) calcium phosphate
k) ammonium sulphite
l) barium permanganate
m) sodium dichromate
n) strontium hydrogensulphite

4 Write ionic formulae for:

a) silver(I) chromate
b) cobalt(II) nitrate
c) chromium(III) sulphate
d) ammonium dichromate
e) iron(II) phosphate
f) lead(II) hydroxide
g) magnesium hydrogencarbonate
h) barium sulphate
i) nickel(II) chloride
j) copper(II) carbonate
k) beryllium fluoride
l) mercury(II) nitrate
m) manganese(II) bromide
n) zinc(II) oxide

21 Ionic and ion–electron equations

- When writing an ionic, or ion–electron, equation it is important to remember that not all of the substances present may be ionic.
- The formulae of all elements and covalent compounds will be the same in both ionic and non-ionic equations.
- Ionic compounds include all salts and solutions of acids like nitric, hydrochloric and sulphuric acids. If a metal is present in a compound, it can be assumed that it is ionic.
- For solid ionic compounds the ionic formula is written in the usual way, but with the state symbol (s) after it, e.g. solid calcium hydroxide is written as $Ca^{2+}(OH^-)_2(s)$.
- For ionic compounds dissolved in water, the ions are separated in a special way and the state symbol (aq) is placed after each ion, e.g. calcium hydroxide solution is written as $Ca^{2+}(aq) + 2OH^-(aq)$.
- Information on solubilities is given in the data booklet under the heading 'Solubilities of selected compounds in water'.

Example 1

Potassium carbonate solution and dilute nitric acid react as follows:

$$K_2CO_3(aq) + 2HNO_3(aq) \rightarrow 2KNO_3(aq) + H_2O(l) + CO_2(g)$$

As an ionic equation this becomes:

$$2K^+(aq) + CO_3^{2-}(aq) + 2H^+(aq) + 2NO_3^-(aq) \rightarrow$$
$$2K^+(aq) + 2NO_3^-(aq) + H_2O(l) + CO_2(g)$$

The potassium and nitrate ions appear on both sides of the equation and can be omitted as they are spectator ions. The reaction then becomes:

$$CO_3^{2-}(aq) + 2H^+(aq) \rightarrow H_2O(l) + CO_2(g)$$

- Ion–electron equations, which show the redox nature of certain reactions, can be derived from the appropriate overall ionic equation. Displacement reactions, for example, are redox in nature since they involve both electron loss (oxidation) and electron gain (reduction).
- Many ion–electron equations are given in the data booklet under the heading 'Electrochemical series'.

Example 2

Magnesium and dilute sulphuric acid react as follows:

$$Mg(s) + H_2SO_4(aq) \rightarrow MgSO_4(aq) + H_2(g)$$

As an ionic equation this becomes:

$$Mg(s) + 2H^+(aq) + SO_4^{2-}(aq) \rightarrow Mg^{2+}(aq) + SO_4^{2-}(aq) + H_2(g)$$

In this equation the sulphate ions appear on both sides of the equation and can be omitted as they are spectator ions. This leaves:

$$Mg(s) + 2H^+(aq) \rightarrow Mg^{2+}(aq) + H_2(g)$$

This is a redox reaction because electrons are lost by magnesium atoms (oxidation) and gained by hydrogen ions (reduction). The ion–electron equations are:

$$Mg(s) \rightarrow Mg^{2+}(aq) + 2e$$
$$2e + 2H^+(aq) \rightarrow H_2(g)$$

QUESTIONS

Copper(II) oxide and dilute hydrochloric acid react to give copper(II) chloride solution and water.

a) Write a balanced equation for this reaction using simple formulae and state symbols.
b) Write a balanced ionic equation for this reaction, again showing state symbols.
c) Which two ions react to form the water molecules in this reaction?

Barium hydroxide solution and dilute sulphuric acid react to form barium sulphate and water.

a) Write a balanced equation for this reaction using simple formulae and state symbols.
b) Write a balanced ionic equation for this reaction, again showing state symbols.
c) Which two ions react to form water molecules in this reaction?
d) The reaction between barium hydroxide solution and dilute sulphuric acid may be described as an example of neutralisation. Into which other category of reaction type does this particular reaction also fall?

Iron reacts with dilute hydrochloric acid to produce iron(II) chloride solution and hydrogen.

a) Write a balanced equation for this reaction using simple formulae and state symbols.
b) Write a balanced ionic equation for this reaction, again showing state symbols.
c) Name the spectator ion in this reaction.
d) Rewrite the ionic equation omitting the spectator ions.

e) Explain the redox nature of the reaction by giving the relevant ion–electron equations, attaching the labels 'reduction' and 'oxidation' as appropriate.

4   The following equation refers to the reaction between copper and silver(I) nitrate solution:

$$Cu(s) + 2AgNO_3(aq) \rightarrow Cu(NO_3)_2(aq) + 2Ag(s)$$

a) Describe the changes that you would expect to observe as this reaction takes place.
b) Write a balanced ionic equation for this reaction, showing state symbols.
c) Rewrite the ionic equation without the spectator ions.
d) Explain the redox nature of the reaction by giving the relevant ion–electron equations, attaching the labels 'reduction' and 'oxidation' as appropriate.

5   All electrolyses involve oxidation and reduction. When nickel(II) bromide solution is electrolysed, the electrode products are nickel and bromine.

a) Give the ion–electron equation for the formation of nickel at the negative electrode, stating whether the process is an example of reduction or oxidation. (State symbols need not be used.)
b) Give similar information regarding the formation of bromine at the positive electrode.

Formula mass and the mole

- The **formula mass** of a substance is obtained by adding the relative atomic masses of the elements in the formula. The number of times a symbol occurs in a formula must be taken into account.

Example 1

Calculate the formula mass of calcium chloride.
Formula $CaCl_2$ (RAMs: Ca = 40; Cl = 35.5)
Formula mass = $40 + (35.5 \times 2) = 111$

Example 2

Calculate the formula mass of ammonium sulphate.
Formula $(NH_4)_2SO_4$ (RAMs: N = 14; H = 1; S = 32; O = 16)
Formula mass = $([14 + (1 \times 4)] \times 2) + 32 + (16 \times 4) = 132$

- A **mole** of a substance is the formula mass in **grams**, e.g. the mass of one mole of calcium chloride is 111 g.
- For any substance, the mass present can be calculated from a knowledge of the number of moles and the formula mass:

    Mass of substance = number of moles × mass of one mole
    = number of moles × formula mass in grams

Example 3

Calculate the mass of 2.5 moles of calcium carbonate, $CaCO_3$.

$$\text{Mass of } CaCO_3 = \text{number of moles} \times \text{formula mass}$$
$$= 2.5 \times [40 + 12 + (16 \times 3)] = 250 \text{ g}$$

- Rearranging the last relationship gives:

$$\text{Number of moles of substance} = \frac{\text{mass of substance in grams}}{\text{formula mass}}$$

From this we can calculate the number of moles of substance present, if we know the mass of substance in grams and the formula mass.

Example 4

Calculate the number of moles of water in 100 g of water.

$$\text{Number of moles of } H_2O = \frac{\text{mass of water in grams}}{\text{formula mass}}$$

$$= \frac{100}{[(1 \times 2) + 16]} = \frac{100}{18} = 5.56$$

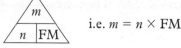

- The relationship between the **mass of substance in grams** (m), the **number of moles of substance** (n) and the **formula mass** (FM) can be summed up in the triangle of knowledge.

i.e. $m = n \times \text{FM}$

QUESTIONS

1 Calculate the formula mass of each of the following substances:

a) nitrogen, N_2
b) ethene, C_2H_4
c) lithium carbonate, Li_2CO_3
d) mercury(II) nitrate, $Hg(NO_3)_2$
e) ammonium phosphate, $(NH_4)_3PO_4$
f) sucrose, $C_{12}H_{22}O_{11}$
g) magnesium hydroxide, $Mg(OH)_2$
h) sulphuric acid, H_2SO_4

2 Calculate the mass of each of the following:

a) 1 mole of sulphur dioxide, SO_2
b) 1.5 moles of argon, Ar
c) 2.25 moles of calcium fluoride, CaF_2
d) 4 moles of iodine, I_2
e) 0.25 moles of calcium phosphate, $Ca_3(PO_4)_2$
f) 0.1 moles of copper(II) hexacyanoferrate(II), $Cu_2Fe(CN)_6$
g) 0.05 moles of magnesium nitrate, $Mg(NO_3)_2$
h) 500 moles of glucose, $C_6H_{12}O_6$

3 Calculate the number of moles of each of the following:

a) 148 g of calcium hydroxide, $Ca(OH)_2$
b) 50.5 g of potassium nitrate, KNO_3
c) 294 g of cyclohexane, C_6H_{12}
d) 1 kg of calcium carbonate, $CaCO_3$
e) 1.83 kg of sodium silicate, Na_2SiO_3
f) 0.195 g of aluminium hydroxide, $Al(OH)_3$
g) 500 g of ammonium carbonate, $(NH_4)_2CO_3$

4 Some farmers buy the fertiliser Nitram (ammonium nitrate, NH_4NO_3) in bags which contain 500 kg. How many moles of ammonium nitrate are in each bag?

5 Aspirin tablets usually contain 300 mg (0.3 g) of the compound acetyl salicylic acid, more commonly known as aspirin. The molecular formula for aspirin is $C_9H_8O_4$. How many moles of aspirin are in each tablet?

6 The average cup of tea or coffee contains about 11 moles of water. What volume does this represent, assuming that 1 g of water occupies 1 cm^3?

23 Calculations based on balanced equations

- A balanced chemical equation tells us the number of moles of each reactant and product in a given reaction.
- A calculation based on a balanced equation can be broken down into five stages:
  1. write a balanced equation for the reaction
  2. identify the number of moles of the substances concerned
  3. replace moles by formula masses in grams
  4. change grams to any other units of mass if necessary
  5. use simple proportion to complete the calculation.

Example 1 (no change of units required)

Calculate the mass of magnesium oxide which is produced when 6 g of magnesium burns in air or oxygen.

$$2Mg + O_2 \rightarrow 2MgO$$
$$2 \text{ mol} \longleftrightarrow 2 \text{ mol}$$
$$48 \text{ g} \longleftrightarrow 80 \text{ g}$$
$$6 \text{ g} \longleftrightarrow \frac{80 \times 6}{48} = 10 \text{ g}$$

Example 2 (change of units required)

What mass of iron would be produced by reducing 320 tonnes of iron(III) oxide in a blast furnace?

$$Fe_2O_3 \quad + 3CO \rightarrow 2Fe + 3CO_2$$
$$1 \text{ mol} \longleftrightarrow 2 \text{ mol}$$
$$160 \text{ g} \longleftrightarrow 112 \text{ g}$$
$$160 \text{ tonnes} \longleftrightarrow 112 \text{ tonnes}$$
$$320 \text{ tonnes} \longleftrightarrow \frac{112 \times 320}{160} = 224 \text{ tonnes}$$

QUESTIONS

1. What mass of water is produced when 160 g of methane burns completely in air?

$$CH_4 + 2O_2 \rightarrow CO_2 + 2H_2O$$

2. Calculate the mass of carbon dioxide produced when 5 g of calcium carbonate reacts with an excess of dilute hydrochloric acid.

$$CaCO_3 + 2HCl \rightarrow CaCl_2 + CO_2 + H_2O$$

3. Calculate the mass of magnesium oxide produced when 100 g of magnesium carbonate is decomposed completely by heating.

$$MgCO_3 \rightarrow MgO + CO_2$$

4 The reaction between zinc and dilute sulphuric acid is often used in school laboratories for the production of hydrogen. What mass of zinc would be needed in order to produce 5 g of hydrogen?

$$Zn + H_2SO_4 \rightarrow ZnSO_4 + H_2$$

5 A dragster can accelerate from a standstill to 270 miles per hour in about five seconds. The fuel is an explosive compound called nitromethane which burns as follows:

$$4CH_3NO_2 + 3O_2 \rightarrow 4CO_2 + 6H_2O + 2N_2$$

During each quarter-mile race 45 kg of fuel is used. Calculate the mass of oxygen needed to burn this mass of fuel.

6 A Perth company buys in ammonia and phosphoric acid, which it reacts together to make the fertiliser ammonium phosphate:

$$3NH_3 + H_3PO_4 \rightarrow (NH_4)_3PO_4$$

What mass of ammonium phosphate fertiliser could be made from 500 kg of ammonia?

7 At Grangemouth BP make large quantities of ethanol by a reaction that is referred to as the 'catalytic hydration' of ethene:

$$C_2H_4 + H_2O \rightarrow C_2H_5OH$$

During one production run 2.8×10^4 tonnes of ethene were used in the process.

a) What mass of ethanol would you expect to be produced if all of the ethene were converted into ethanol?
b) What mass of ethanol would be produced if the process were only 95% efficient?

8 During World War II US pilots carried lithium hydride tablets. If any aeroplane crash landed in the sea, the lithium hydride would react with seawater and fill lifebelts and lifeboats with hydrogen.

$$LiH(s) + H_2O(l) \rightarrow LiOH(aq) + H_2(g)$$

a) What mass of hydrogen, in grams, would be released using 1 kg of lithium hydride?
b) If, under operational conditions, 1 g of hydrogen occupied 12 l, calculate the volume of hydrogen which would be produced from 1 kg of lithium hydride. (1 litre = 1 dm^3)

Concentration and the mole

- It is generally more useful to give the concentration of a solution in moles per litre (mol/l) than in grams per litre (g/l), e.g. a 2 mol/l solution contains 2 moles of solute per litre of solution.
- The relationship between **concentration of solution** (C), **number of moles of solute** (n) and **volume of solution** (V) is:

$$\text{concentration of solution} = \frac{\text{number of moles of solute}}{\text{volume of solution (in litres)}}$$

Example 1

Calculate the concentration of a citric acid solution, given that 1.5 moles of citric acid are dissolved in water and made up to a final volume of 3 l.

$$\text{Concentration of citric acid, } C = \frac{n}{V} = \frac{1.5}{3} = 0.5 \text{ mol/l}$$

Example 2

Calculate the concentration of a solution of sodium hydroxide, NaOH, given that it contains 12 g of NaOH in 500 cm^3 of solution.

$$\text{Number of moles of NaOH, } n = \frac{\text{mass of NaOH in grams } (m)}{\text{formula mass of NaOH (FM)}}$$

$$= \frac{12}{40} = 0.3$$

$$\text{Concentration of NaOH solution, } C = \frac{n}{V} = \frac{0.3}{0.5} = 0.6 \text{ mol/l}$$

Note: 500 cm^3 = 0.5 l

Example 3

Calculate the volume of solution produced if 53 g of sodium carbonate, Na_2CO_3, are used to make a solution with a concentration of 0.25 mol/l.

$$\text{Number of moles of } Na_2CO_3, n = \frac{m}{FM} = \frac{53}{106} = 0.5$$

$$\text{Volume of } Na_2CO_3 \text{ solution, } V = \frac{n}{C} = \frac{0.5}{0.25} = 2 \text{ l}$$

1 Calculate the concentration of each of the following in mol/l:

a) 1 l of a solution containing 3 moles of solute
b) 2 l of a solution containing 1 mole of solute
c) 500 cm^3 of a solution containing 2.5 moles of solute
d) 100 cm^3 of a solution containing 0.04 moles of solute.

2 Calculate the number of moles of solute in each of the following:

a) 2 l of a solution with a concentration of 1.5 mol/l
b) 5 l of a solution with a concentration of 0.2 mol/l
c) 250 cm^3 of a solution with a concentration of 0.105 mol/l
d) 10 cm^3 of a solution with a concentration of 8 mol/l.

3 Calculate the volume of solution which could be produced using:

a) 2 moles of solute in a solution of 0.4 mol/l concentration
b) 7.5 moles of solute in a solution of 0.25 mol/l concentration
c) 0.6 moles of solute in a solution of 2 mol/l concentration
d) 0.03 moles of solute in a solution of 0.015 mol/l concentration.

4 Calculate the concentration of each of the following in mol/l:

a) 2.5 l of a solution containing 280 g of KOH
b) 0.02 l of a solution containing 6 g of $MgSO_4$
c) 50 cm^3 of a solution containing 3.4 g of NH_3
d) 800 cm^3 of a solution containing 100 g of $(NH_4)_2SO_3$.

5 Calculate the mass of solute in each of the following solutions:

a) 2.25 l of 0.1 mol/l HNO_3
b) 10 l of 18 mol/l H_2SO_4
c) 650 cm^3 of 0.2 mol/l $Ba(NO_3)_2$ (RAM of Ba = 137)
d) 200 cm^3 of 4.5 mol/l NaOH.

6 Calculate the volume of solution which could be produced using:

a) 568 g of Na_2SO_4 in a solution of 2 mol/l concentration
b) 3.7 g of $Ca(OH)_2$ in a solution of 0.02 mol/l concentration
c) 200 g of $NaHCO_3$ in a solution of 0.6 mol/l concentration
d) 1.2 kg of $C_6H_{12}O_6$ in a solution of 1.4 mol/l concentration.

Calculations based on titration results

- The relationship between **concentration of solution** (C), **number of moles of solute** (n) and **volume of solution** (V) can be used in calculations based on titration results.

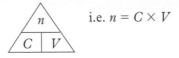

i.e. $n = C \times V$

Example 1

20 cm³ of sodium hydroxide solution was neutralised by 15 cm³ of 0.1 mol/l sulphuric acid. Calculate the concentration of the sodium hydroxide solution. First write a balanced equation for the reaction:

$$H_2SO_4 + 2NaOH \rightarrow Na_2SO_4 + 2H_2O$$
$$\text{1 mol} \qquad \text{2 mol}$$

Number of moles of acid reacting, $n_{H_2SO_4} = C \times V$

$$= 0.1 \times 0.015 = 0.0015$$

From the equation: 1 mol H_2SO_4 reacts with 2 mol NaOH
Thus: 0.0015 mol H_2SO_4 reacts with 0.0030 mol NaOH

$$\text{Concentration of NaOH, } C_{NaOH} = \frac{n_{NaOH}}{V} = \frac{0.0030}{0.02} = 0.15 \text{ mol/l}$$

Alternative method

- In titrations we usually know the volume of acid (V_A) and the volume of alkali or soluble base (V_B). We also usually know either the concentration of the acid (C_A) or the concentration of the alkali (C_B).
- From the balanced equation for the reaction, we can find the number of moles of acid (a) and the number of moles of alkali (b) which react together.
- Using the relationship $n = C \times V$, we can write the ratio of moles of acid to moles of alkali required for neutralisation as:

$$\frac{C_A \times V_A}{C_B \times V_B} = \frac{a}{b}$$

From this relationship we can calculate any of the six quantities if the other five are known.

Note: Because the relationship is a ratio, there is no need to convert the volumes into litres. Any units of volume may be used for V_A and V_B, but they must be the same units in each case.

Example 2

Use the alternative method for the calculation given in the previous example. As before, write a balanced equation for the reaction:

$$H_2SO_4 + 2NaOH \rightarrow Na_2SO_4 + 2H_2O$$

1 mol   2 mol

$a = 1$ $b = 2$

Rearranging $\dfrac{C_A \times V_A}{C_B \times V_B} = \dfrac{a}{b}$ gives: $\quad C_B = \dfrac{C_A \times V_A \times b}{V_B \times a}$

$$= \frac{0.1 \times 15 \times 2 \text{ mol/l}}{20 \times 1}$$

$$= 0.15 \text{ mol/l}$$

QUESTIONS

1 20 cm³ of 0.2 mol/l sodium hydroxide solution neutralised 10 cm³ of nitric acid, the balanced equation for the reaction being:

$$HNO_3 + NaOH \rightarrow NaNO_3 + H_2O$$

Calculate:

a) the number of moles of alkali present
b) the number of moles of acid reacting
c) the concentration of the acid.

2 10 cm³ of potassium hydroxide solution neutralised 40 cm³ of 0.1 mol/l phosphoric acid, the balanced equation for the reaction being:

$$H_3PO_4 + 3KOH \rightarrow K_3PO_4 + 3H_2O$$

a) How many moles of alkali react with one mole of acid?
b) How many moles of acid are present?
c) How many moles of alkali react in the titration?
d) Calculate the concentration of the alkali.

3 16 cm³ of 0.5 mol/l ammonia solution neutralised 25 cm³ of sulphuric acid, the balanced equation for the reaction being:

$$H_2SO_4 + 2NH_3 \rightarrow (NH_4)_2SO_4$$

Calculate the concentration of the sulphuric acid.

4 Calculate the volume of 0.25 mol/l nitric acid that would be needed to neutralise 25 cm³ of 0.2 mol/l barium hydroxide solution. The balanced equation for the reaction is:

$$2HNO_3 + Ba(OH)_2 \rightarrow Ba(NO_3)_2 + 2H_2O$$

5 Calculate the volume of 0.2 mol/l sulphuric acid that would be needed to neutralise 50 cm³ of a 0.05 mol/l solution of calcium hydroxide. The balanced equation for the reaction is:

$$H_2SO_4 + Ca(OH)_2 \rightarrow CaSO_4 + 2H_2O$$

6 A printing company uses concentrated ammonia solution in one particular process. The company selling the ammonia solution checks its concentration in the following way:

I   The concentrated ammonia solution is diluted exactly 100 times.
II   The diluted solution of ammonia is titrated with 0.1 mol/l hydrochloric acid.

In one check it was found that 20 cm³ of the diluted ammonia solution required 25 cm³ of 0.1 mol/l hydrochloric acid for neutralisation. Calculate the concentration of the concentrated ammonia solution, given that the balanced equation for the neutralisation reaction is:

$$NH_3 + HCl \rightarrow NH_4Cl$$

Percentage composition by mass

- The percentage, by mass, of an element in a compound can be calculated as follows:

$$\% \text{ by mass of element} = \frac{\text{mass of element in formula}}{\text{formula mass}} \times 100$$

Example 1

Calculate the percentage, by mass, of magnesium in magnesium oxide, MgO.

$$\% \text{ by mass of Mg} = \frac{24}{40} \times 100$$

$$= 60\%$$

Example 2

Calculate the percentage, by mass, of nitrogen in ammonium nitrate, NH_4NO_3.

$$\% \text{ by mass of N} = \frac{(2 \times 14)}{80} \times 100 \text{ (\textbf{two} N atoms present)}$$

$$= \frac{28}{80} \times 100 = 35\%$$

Example 3

Calculate the percentage, by mass, of calcium in calcium phosphate, $Ca_3(PO_4)_2$.

$$\% \text{ by mass of Ca} = \frac{(3 \times 40)}{310} \times 100 \text{ (\textbf{three} Ca atoms present)}$$

$$= \frac{120}{310} \times 100 = 38.7\%$$

- If you have to calculate the percentage, by mass, of **all** of the elements in a compound, the last one may be obtained by subtraction from 100.

Example 4

Calculate the percentage, by mass, of both elements in ethene, C_2H_4.

$$\% \text{ by mass of C} = \frac{(2 \times 12)}{28} \times 100 = 85.7\%$$

$$\% \text{ by mass of H} = 100 - 85.7 = 14.3\%$$

1 Calculate the percentage, by mass, of:

  a) carbon in methane, CH_4
  b) calcium in calcium carbonate, $CaCO_3$
  c) oxygen in water, H_2O
  d) nitrogen in ammonia, NH_3
  e) sulphur in sulphur dioxide, SO_2
  f) magnesium in magnesium nitride, Mg_3N_2
  g) potassium in potassium sulphate, K_2SO_4
  h) nitrogen in ammonium phosphate, $(NH_4)_3PO_4$
  i) carbon in glucose, $C_6H_{12}O_6$
  j) oxygen in calcium nitrate, $Ca(NO_3)_2$
  k) hydrogen in ammonium carbonate, $(NH_4)_2CO_3$
  l) phosphorus in magnesium phosphate, $Mg_3(PO_4)_2$

2 Calculate the percentage, by mass, of all the elements in:

  a) carbon monoxide, CO
  b) hydrogen chloride, HCl
  c) magnesium fluoride, MgF_2
  d) aluminium oxide, Al_2O_3
  e) sodium oxide, Na_2O
  f) lithium nitrate, $LiNO_3$
  g) ammonium chloride, NH_4Cl
  h) calcium sulphate, $CaSO_4$
  i) ammonium sulphate, $(NH_4)_2SO_4$
  j) magnesium hydrogencarbonate, $Mg(HCO_3)_2$
  k) sucrose, $C_{12}H_{22}O_{11}$
  l) calcium dihydrogenphosphate, $Ca(H_2PO_4)_2$

Empirical formulae

- An **empirical formula** shows the simplest whole number ratio of atoms in a compound, e.g. ethene has the molecular formula C_2H_4, so its empirical formula is CH_2 since there is one carbon atom to two hydrogen atoms.
- Empirical formulae can be worked out from the masses of each element in a given compound or from the percentage, by mass, of each element.

Example I

Determine the empirical formula of an oxide of silver, given that it contains 93.1% by mass of silver and 6.9% by mass of oxygen.

element	Ag	O
mass in g	93.1	6.9
number of moles of atoms	$\frac{93.1}{108} = 0.862$	$\frac{6.9}{16} = 0.431$
simplest whole number ratio	$\frac{0.862}{0.431} = 2$	$\frac{0.431}{0.431} = 1$

divide by RAM

divide by the smaller number

Thus the empirical formula is Ag_2O.

- There are situations where it is necessary to multiply by a small number, such as 2 or 3, after division by the smaller of the number of moles of atoms.

Example 2

Determine the empirical formula of an oxide of iron, given that 2.80 g of iron were found to combine with 1.20 g of oxygen.

element	Fe	O
mass in g	2.80	1.20
number of moles of atoms	$\frac{2.80}{56} = 0.05$	$\frac{1.20}{16} = 0.075$
simplest whole number ratio	$\frac{0.05}{0.05} = 1$	$\frac{0.075}{0.05} = 1.5$
multiply by 2	$1 \times 2 = 2$	$1.5 \times 2 = 3$

divide by RAM

divide by the smaller number

Thus the empirical formula is Fe_2O_3.

- The empirical formula can be used to determine the molecular formula if the formula mass is known.

Example 3

Determine the molecular formula of a hydrocarbon, given that the empirical formula is CH_2 and the formula mass is 42.

Since the empirical formula is CH_2, the molecular formula must be C_nH_{2n}, where n is a whole number.

$$\text{Formula mass of } C_nH_{2n} = (12 \times n) + (1 \times 2 \times n) = 42$$
$$14n = 42$$
$$n = 3$$

Thus the molecular formula of the hydrocarbon is C_3H_6.

QUESTIONS

1 For each of the following determine the empirical formula of the compound from the percentage composition by mass given:

a) C (75%), H (25%)
b) C (80%), H (20%)
c) Cu (62.75%), F (37.25%)
d) Ca (20%), Br (80%)
e) P (56.4%), O (43.6%)
f) Hg (44.2%), I (55.8%).

2 For each of the following determine the empirical formula of the compound from the masses of the elements present in a certain mass of compound:

a) C (3 g), O (4 g)
b) S (2 g), O (3 g)
c) Ni (2.95 g), Cl (3.55 g)
d) Al (18 g), S (32 g)
e) Cu (4.3 g), S (2.15 g)
f) N (0.368 g), Cl (2.803 g).

3 10.0 g of an iodide of lead was analysed and found to contain 4.49 g of lead. Determine the empirical formula of the compound.

4 4.40 g of calcium was heated in a stream of hydrogen to produce calcium hydride. When the reaction was complete it was found that the mass of calcium hydride produced was 4.62 g. Determine the empirical formula of calcium hydride.

5 4.00 g of iron wire was heated in a stream of hydrogen chloride producing 9.07 g of a chloride of iron. Determine the empirical formula of this compound.

6 3.75 g of an oxide of nickel was reduced by heating in a stream of carbon monoxide and gave 2.95 g of nickel when reduction was complete. Determine the empirical formula of the nickel oxide.

7 a) A hydrocarbon was analysed and found to contain 85.71% by mass of carbon. Determine the empirical formula of the hydrocarbon.
   b) Given that the formula mass of the hydrocarbon is 70, determine its molecular formula.

8 Analysis of a two-element compound showed that it contained 2.20 g of boron and 0.60 g of hydrogen.

   a) Determine the empirical formula of the compound (RAM of B = 11).
   b) Given that the formula mass of the compound is 28, determine the molecular formula.

Types of chemical formulae

Molecular formula shows the number of atoms of the different elements which are present in one molecule of a substance, e.g. C_2H_4 for ethene.

Empirical formula shows the simplest whole number ratio of atoms in a compound, e.g. CH_2 for ethene.

> **Ionic formula** shows the simplest whole number ratio of ions in a compound, e.g. $Ca^{2+}(Cl^-)_2$ for calcium chloride.

Full structural formula shows all the bonds present in a molecule or ion but does not necessarily show the true shape, e.g. for methane:

$$
\begin{array}{c}
\text{H} \\
| \\
\text{H}-\text{C}-\text{H} \\
| \\
\text{H}
\end{array}
$$

Shortened structural formula shows the sequence of groups of atoms in a molecule, e.g. $CH_3CH_2CH_2CH_3$ for butane.

Perspective formula shows the true shape of a molecule or ion, e.g. for methane (tetrahedral shape):

Note: What do you write when asked for 'the formula' or 'the simple formula' of a substance?

a) For a **covalent molecular substance**, we usually give the molecular formula, e.g. C_2H_6 for ethane. However, sometimes the empirical formula is used instead, e.g. P_2O_3 for phosphorus oxide when in fact the molecular formula is P_4O_6.

b) For an **ionic or covalent network compound**, we usually write the empirical formula, e.g. NaCl for sodium chloride and SiO_2 for silicon dioxide.

c) For **elements**, a single symbol is usually written for all apart from those which exist as diatomic molecules, e.g. C for carbon, and Fe for iron, but H_2 for hydrogen and O_2 for oxygen, etc. (Only the noble gases exist as individual atoms not bonded to other atoms. In all other cases where single symbols are written as chemical formulae for elements, the symbol represents a sort of empirical formula.)

QUESTIONS

Oxalic acid occurs in rhubarb and its full structural formula is as follows:

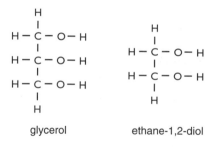

a) Give the molecular formula for oxalic acid.
b) Give the empirical formula for oxalic acid.

Glycerol and ethane-1,2-diol, which is used as 'antifreeze', are special kinds of alcohols. Their full structural formulae are as follows:

```
      H
      |
  H — C — O—H            H
      |                  |
  H — C — O—H        H — C — O—H
      |                  |
  H — C — O—H        H — C — O—H
      |                  |
      H                  H

    glycerol         ethane-1,2-diol
```

a) Give the molecular formula for glycerol.
b) Give the empirical formula for ethane-1,2-diol.
c) The shortened structural formula for glycerol is usually given as $CH_2OHCHOHCH_2OH$. Give a similar shortened structural formula for ethane-1,2-diol.

3 In all alkane molecules the carbon atoms are surrounded, tetrahedrally, by four single covalent bonds. Use this information to help you draw a perspective formula for ethane, that is a formula which shows the true shape of the molecule.

4 a) Give the molecular formula for propene.
   b) Give the empirical formula for hexane.
   c) Give the shortened structural formula for octane.
   d) Give the full structural formula for pentane.

5 The ammonium ion has the same shape as a methane molecule. Draw the perspective formula for the ammonium ion.

29 Types of chemical reaction

Addition   A reaction in which two or more molecules join to produce a single larger molecule and nothing else.

Combustion   The burning of a substance during which it combines with oxygen.

Corrosion   The process whereby the surface of a metal changes from an element to a compound.

Cracking   The breaking up of hydrocarbon molecules to produce a mixture of smaller molecules.

Decomposition   The breaking down of a compound into two or more substances.

Displacement   The formation of a metal from a solution containing its ions by reaction with a metal higher in the electrochemical series.

Fermentation   The breakdown of glucose to form alcohol and carbon dioxide, brought about by the presence of yeast.

Neutralisation   A reaction that moves the pH of a solution towards 7.

Photosynthesis   The process whereby green plants convert carbon dioxide and water into carbohydrates, such as glucose, and release oxygen into the air.

Precipitation   The reaction of two solutions to form an insoluble product called a precipitate.

Respiration   The process whereby carbohydrates, such as glucose, are broken down by reaction with oxygen to release energy. Carbon dioxide and water are formed during the process.

Rusting   The corrosion of iron.

Addition polymerisation   A process whereby many small monomer molecules join to form one large polymer molecule and nothing else.

Condensation   A reaction in which two or more molecules join to form a single larger molecule, with water, or another small molecule, formed at the same time.

Condensation polymerisation   A process whereby many small monomer molecules join to form one large polymer molecule, with water, or another small molecule, formed at the same time.

c

Hydrolysis   A reaction in which a large molecule is broken down into two or more smaller molecules by reaction with water.

Oxidation   A reaction in which electrons are lost.

Reduction   A reaction in which electrons are gained.

Redox   A reaction in which electrons are lost by one substance and gained by another.

QUESTIONS

A	$HCl + KOH \rightarrow KCl + H_2O$
B	$CH_4 + 2O_2 \rightarrow CO_2 + 2H_2O$
C	$C_3H_6 + H_2 \rightarrow C_3H_8$
D	$NaCl(aq) + AgNO_3(aq) \rightarrow AgCl(s) + NaNO_3(aq)$
E	$C_5H_{12} \rightarrow C_2H_4 + C_3H_8$
F	$CaCO_3 \rightarrow CaO + CO_2$

Identify the following types of chemical reaction in the grid above:

a) cracking
b) precipitation
c) combustion
d) neutralisation
e) addition.

Name the type of chemical reaction in each of the following examples:

a) propene $\rightarrow$ poly(propene)
b) $C + O_2 \rightarrow CO_2$
c) glucose + oxygen $\rightarrow$ carbon dioxide + water
     (*two* answers)
d) $NaOH(aq) + HNO_3(aq) \rightarrow$
       $NaNO_3(aq) + H_2O(l)$
e) $C_2H_6 \rightarrow C_2H_4 + H_2$
f) glucose $\rightarrow$ alcohol + carbon dioxide
g) $BaCl_2(aq) + K_2SO_4(aq) \rightarrow$
       $BaSO_4(s) + 2KCl(aq)$
h) $C_2H_4 + Br_2 \rightarrow C_2H_4Br_2$
i) carbon dioxide + water $\rightarrow$ glucose + oxygen
j) $2HgO \rightarrow 2Hg + O_2$

The following questions require knowledge of ALL types of chemical reaction in the Standard Grade Chemistry course.

3

A	$C_{12}H_{22}O_{11} + H_2O \rightarrow 2C_6H_{12}O_6$
B	$Cu(s) + 2Ag^+(aq) \rightarrow Cu^{2+}(aq) + 2Ag(s)$
C	$nCH_2{=}CHCl \rightarrow ({-}CH_2{-}CHCl{-})_n$
D	$6CO_2 + 6H_2O \rightarrow C_6H_{12}O_6 + 6O_2$
E	$C_6H_{12}O_6 \rightarrow 2C_2H_5OH + 2CO_2$
F	$SO_3^{2-} + H_2O \rightarrow SO_4^{2-} + 2H^+ + 2e$

Identify the following types of chemical reaction in the grid above:

a) addition polymerisation   d) redox
b) oxidation   e) photosynthesis.
c) hydrolysis

4 Name the type of chemical reaction in each of the following examples:

a) $nC_6H_{12}O_6 \rightarrow (C_6H_{10}O_5)_n + nH_2O$
b) $C_6H_{12}O_6 + C_6H_{12}O_6 \rightarrow C_{12}H_{22}O_{11} + H_2O$
c) $(NH_4)_2Cr_2O_7 \rightarrow Cr_2O_3 + N_2 + 4H_2O$
d) $6e + Cr_2O_7^{2-} + 14H^+ \rightarrow 2Cr^{3+} + 7H_2O$
e) $Ca(OH)_2 + H_2SO_4 \rightarrow CaSO_4 + 2H_2O$
f) $Zn(s) + 2HCl(aq) \rightarrow ZnCl_2(aq) + H_2(g)$
     (*three* answers)
g) $Na_2CO_3(aq) + 2HNO_3(aq) \rightarrow$
       $2NaNO_3(aq) + H_2O(l) + CO_2(g)$
h) $CH_3COOH + C_2H_5OH \rightarrow$
       $CH_3COOC_2H_5 + H_2O$
i) $H^+(aq) + OH^-(aq) \rightarrow H_2O(l)$
j) $C_{12}H_{26} \rightarrow C_6H_{14} + C_3H_8 + C_2H_4 + C$

Identification tests

Flame tests: certain metals can be identified by the characteristic colours produced when they, or their compounds, are heated in a bunsen flame e.g. sodium produces a yellow colour and potassium produces a lilac colour. (Flame colours are given in the data booklet.)

Carbon dioxide turns lime water milky.

Hydrogen burns with a pop (when a lighted taper is applied).

Oxygen re-lights a glowing taper.

Carbonate releases carbon dioxide gas with dilute acid (such as hydrochloric acid).

pH: the approximate pH value for a solution can be found using pH paper or universal/pH indicator. A typical colour range is:

pH	colour
0–4	red
5	orange
6	yellow
7	green
8	green-blue
9	blue
10	indigo
11–14	violet

Sugars e.g. glucose, produce an orange-red colour when heated with Benedict's (or Fehling's) solution. **Note:** sucrose does **not** give this result.

Starch produces a dark blue colour with iodine solution.

C=C bond decolorises bromine solution rapidly.

Rust: rust indicator (ferroxyl indicator) turns blue. (When iron rusts, Fe^{2+}(aq) and OH^-(aq) are formed.)

Fe^{2+}(aq) produces a blue colour with ferroxyl indicator.

OH^-(aq) produces a pink colour with ferroxyl indicator.

Water has a freezing point of $0°C$ and a boiling point of $100°C$.

Ammonium salt releases alkaline ammonia gas when heated with sodium hydroxide (or similar alkali).

1   The grid below contains full structural formulae for six gases.

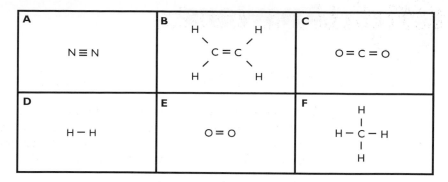

Identify the gas which:

a) re-lights a glowing taper
b) turns lime water milky
c) burns with a pop
d) decolorises bromine solution.

2   A sweet-tasting carbohydrate was subjected to two tests:

I It gave no colour change when tested with iodine solution.
II It gave no colour change when heated with Benedict's solution.

a) What can you conclude from test I alone?
b) Suggest a possible name for the sweet-tasting carbohydrate.

3   With the help of the data booklet, name the flame colours produced by the following compounds:

a) lithium chloride
b) calcium carbonate
c) barium nitrate
d) copper oxide.

4   Gas cookers can produce a lot of condensation in kitchens. How would you prove that the colourless liquid obtained was water? State the tests that you would do and give the results.

5   The white solid known as 'smelling salts' is ammonium carbonate.

a) Name the gas produced when smelling salts are warmed with an alkali such as sodium hydroxide (smelling salts actually give off this gas slowly in the absence of heat or an alkali).
b) Describe a test to show that the white solid is a carbonate and give the results of the test.

6   Sarah set up the following experiment as part of an investigation into corrosion.

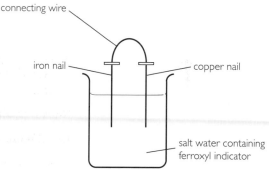

From the results of the experiment Sarah deduced that the following reactions were taking place:

At the iron nail: $Fe(s) \rightarrow Fe^{2+}(aq) + 2e$
At the copper nail: $4e + O_2(aq) + 2H_2O(l)$
$\rightarrow 4OH^-(aq)$

What colours did Sarah see around each nail? Explain your answers.

part 1 Answers

1 Introducing chemistry

1 New substance formed (a white substance); change in appearance from silver to white; energy change/heat given out.

2 B and E

3 a) carbon and sulphur
   b) hydrogen, beryllium, nitrogen, oxygen, fluorine, magnesium and chlorine
   c) neon

4 a) hydrogen; b) oxygen; c) nitrogen;
   d) fluorine; e) phosphorus; f) sulphur;
   g) iodine; h) uranium; i) vanadium.

5 a)

Compound	Elements present	
hydrogen oxide	hydrogen	oxygen
lead chloride	lead	chlorine
sodium sulphide	sodium	sulphur
calcium bromide	calcium	bromine

   b)

Compound	Elements present		
lithium sulphate	lithium	sulphur	oxygen
zinc carbonate	zinc	carbon	oxygen
copper nitrate	copper	nitrogen	oxygen
barium sulphite	barium	sulphur	oxygen
potassium nitrite	potassium	nitrogen	oxygen

6 There are many examples, vinegar, bleach, tea, coffee, lemonade, etc.

7 a) D; b) C

2 The speed of reactions

1 a) C; b) A; c) B

2 a) D; b) A

3 a) A substance which speeds up a reaction (without itself being changed).
   b) Select two identical pieces of zinc and attach a piece of copper to one of them. Place these in separate test tubes containing equal volumes of dilute sulphuric acid, of the same concentration, and at the same temperature.

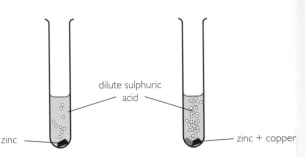

4 B and D

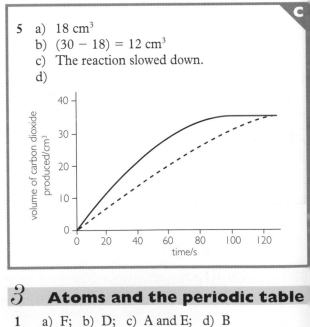

5 a) 18 cm^3
   b) (30 − 18) = 12 cm^3
   c) The reaction slowed down.
   d)

3 Atoms and the periodic table

1 a) F; b) D; c) A and E; d) B

2 a) E; b) C; c) B; d) F; e) A

3 . . . periodic table . . . atomic . . . electrons . . . group . . . outer . . . similar . . .

4 a) in the nucleus
   b) electrons
   c) The positive charge of the nucleus is equal to the sum of the negative charges of the electrons.

5 a) Thallium and polonium are metals; tellurium is a non-metal.
   b) Astatine and francium do not occur naturally.
   c) caesium (and presumably francium as well).
   d) (i) 2,3; (ii) 2,8,5; (iii) 2,8,8,2
   e) 6
   f) helium

6 a) 1823
   b) Germanium and silicon are in the same group and have the same number of outer electrons.

7 a) A and C; b) A and B; c) E and F;
   d) B and D
8 a) germanium; b) 32; c) 2,8,18,4;
   d) strontium; e) Sr; f) 2,8,18,8,2
9 a) 14; b) 6; c) 6; d) 8; e) 6; f) $^{21}_{10}$Ne;
   g) 10; h) 10; i) 11; j) $^{56}_{26}$Fe; k) 56;
   l) 26; m) 26
10 a) 19; b) 20; c) 18; d) $^{25}_{12}$Mg^{2+}
11 a) 35; b) 44; c) 36; d) $^{31}_{15}$P^{3-}
12 ^{63}Cu is present in greater amount because the relative atomic mass is closer to 63 than 65.
13 The accurate value for the relative atomic mass must be just below 80. This is because it must be nearer to the mass number of the more abundant isotope.

4 How atoms combine

1 a) A molecule which contains only two atoms.
   b) CO

2 C and D

3

Substance	Molecular formula	Structure of molecule
fluorine	F_2	F—F
bromine	Br_2	Br—Br
hydrogen fluoride	HF	H—F
hydrogen bromide	HBr	H—Br

4 a) carbon, hydrogen and oxygen
   b) covalent bonds
   c) 24
   d) $24 \times 8 = 192$

5 Each molecule contains one carbon atom, one hydrogen atom and three chlorine atoms.

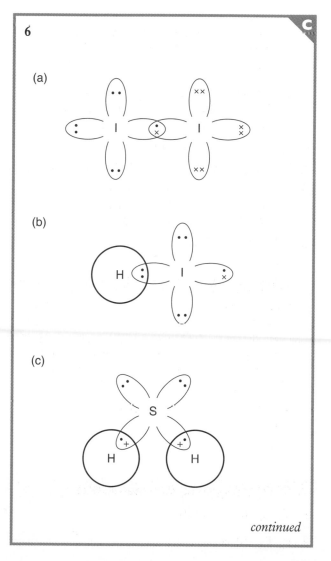

continued

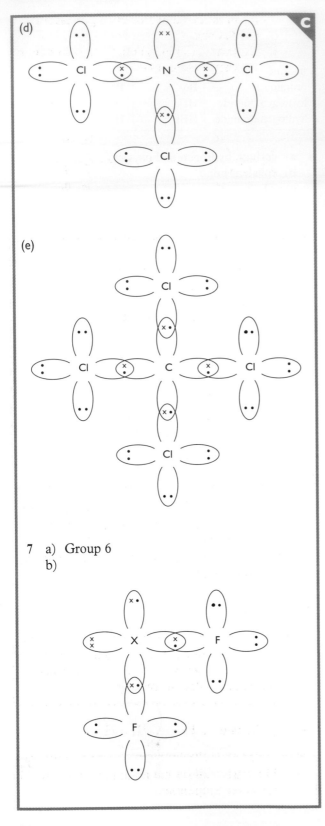

(d)

(e)

7 a) Group 6
  b)

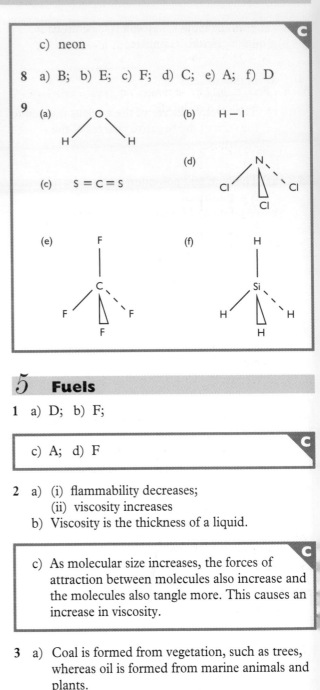

c) neon

8 a) B; b) E; c) F; d) C; e) A; f) D

9 (a)

(b) H — I

(c) S = C = S

(d)

(e)

(f)

5 Fuels

1 a) D; b) F;

c) A; d) F

2 a) (i) flammability decreases;
     (ii) viscosity increases
  b) Viscosity is the thickness of a liquid.

c) As molecular size increases, the forces of attraction between molecules also increase and the molecules also tangle more. This causes an increase in viscosity.

3 a) Coal is formed from vegetation, such as trees, whereas oil is formed from marine animals and plants.
  b) Various answers possible. For example, burning coal can produce dirty smoke and poisonous sulphur dioxide, which is a cause of acid rain; oil spillages at sea can pollute beaches and have a devastating effect on wildlife such as birds and sea creatures; burning petrol and diesel can release sulphur dioxide and equally harmful nitrogen dioxide into the air.

4   a) Carbon dioxide, water and sulphur dioxide.
    b) Sulphur dioxide is poisonous and acidic
        (see 3(b) above).

5   a) Bars should be separate, not joined. Bars and
        axes should be labelled.

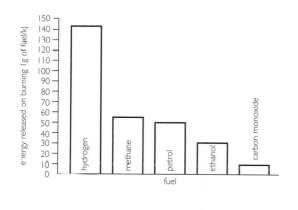

    b) A fuel is a chemical which burns giving out
        energy.
    c) hydrogen
    d) carbon monoxide

6   a) carbon dioxide and nitrogen
    b) $2CO + 2NO \rightarrow 2CO_2 + N_2$

7   On short journeys the catalysts do not become hot
    enough to operate efficiently.

6   Hydrocarbons

1   a) B and F;   b) A;

    c) C and E

2   a)

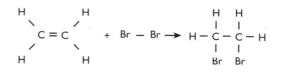

    b) $CH_3CH_2CH_2CH{=}CH_2$;   c) $C_{21}H_{44}$;
    d) C_8H_{16};   e) CH_2

3   a) hexane;   b) pentene

4   a) An unsaturated hydrocarbon possesses a
        $C{=}C$ bond.
    b) Test with bromine solution – decolorisation
        indicates unsaturation.

5

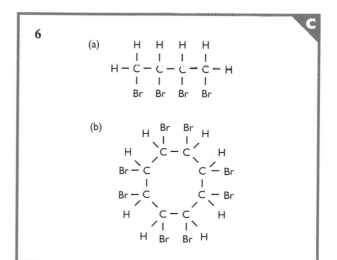

6   (a)
    (b)

7   a) Cracking is a method for producing smaller
        molecules from hydrocarbons in crude oil.
    b) Crude oil contains more long-chain
        hydrocarbons than are useful for present-day
        industrial processes.

8   a) hexane

    b) There were not enough hydrogen atoms in
        the alkane molecule to produce two smaller
        alkane molecules on cracking.

9   a) Propane: $C_3H_8 \rightarrow C_3H_6 + H_2$

    b) The catalyst allows the reaction to take place
        at a lower temperature.

10 **C**

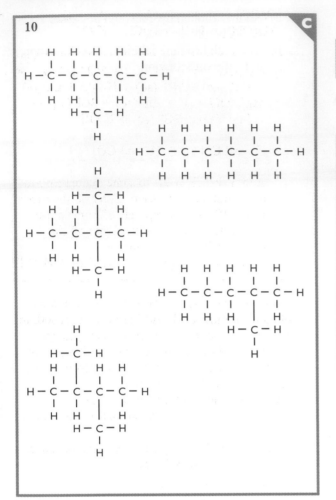

7 Properties of substances

1 a) E; b) C; c) D; d) B; the remaining substance, A, might be mercury

2 a) E; b) C and D

3 B and F **C**

4 a) C; b) A

5 a) Electrolysis is the process by which ionic compounds conduct electricity, with chemical reactions taking place at the electrodes.
b) The ions are not free to move and therefore cannot carry the current.
c) chlorine

d) They would react together.

e) (i) $Na^+ + e \rightarrow Na$; (ii) $2Cl^- \rightarrow Cl_2 + 2e$ **C**

6 a) An electrolyte is a substance that conducts by movement of ions.

b) $Al^{3+} + 3e \rightarrow Al$ **C**

7 a) The copper ions are blue and positively charged. Reasons: (i) sodium nitrate is colourless indicating that sodium ions and nitrate ions are colourless – the blue colour of copper nitrate is therefore due to the copper ion; (ii) since the blue copper ions moved towards the negative electrode they must have a positive charge.
b) The dichromate ions are orange and negatively charged. Reasons: (i) since sodium ions are colourless, the orange colour of sodium dichromate must be due to the dichromate ion; (ii) the orange dichromate ions move towards the positive electrode and must therefore possess a negative charge.

8 Acids and alkalis

1 D and F

2 a) the hydrogen ion, $H^+(aq)$
b) Use pH paper or universal indicator. The result could be an orange or red colour.
c) Apply a lighted taper to the gas. Hydrogen burns with a pop.

d) $2H^+ + 2e \rightarrow H_2$ **C**

3 a) lithium oxide + water → lithium hydroxide
b) $Li_2O + H_2O \rightarrow LiOH$

4 $CaO(s) + H_2O(l) \rightarrow Ca(OH)_2(aq)$ **C**

5 a) The hydroxide ion, $OH^-(aq)$

b)

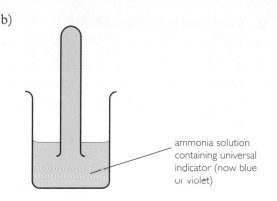

ammonia solution containing universal indicator (now blue or violet)

6 All four values must be below 7, with boracic acid having the highest pH value, followed by ethanoic acid, then citric acid and, lastly, hydrochloric acid. Possible pH values are:

boracic acid   pH 5
ethanoic acid   pH 4
citric acid   pH 3
hydrochloric acid   pH 1

7 a) The level of acidity decreases.
     b) the pH increases.

     c) The hydrogen ion concentration decreases. **C**

8 $ClO_4^-(aq)$

9   Reactions of acids

1 a) A and F;   b) C

2 a) lithium chloride + water
     b) aluminium nitrate + water
     c) strontium sulphate + water + carbon dioxide
     d) zinc chloride + hydrogen

3 a) $CaCl_2(aq) + H_2O(l)$
     b) $HNO_3(aq) ... H_2O(l)$
     c) $K_2CO_3(aq) ... H_2O(l)$
     d) $HCl(aq) ... H_2(g)$

4 a) calcium carbonate + hydrochloric acid →
       calcium chloride + water + carbon dioxide
       magnesium hydroxide + hydrochloric acid →
       magnesium chloride + water

     b) $CaCO_3 + HCl → CaCl_2 + H_2O + CO_2$;
       $Mg(OH)_2 + HCl → MgCl_2 + H_2O$

     c) $Ca^{2+}CO_3^{2-}(s) + 2H^+(aq) + 2Cl^-(aq) →$ **C**
         $Ca^{2+}(aq) + 2Cl^-(aq) + H_2O(l) + CO_2(g)$
         $Mg^{2+}(OH^-)_2(s) + 2H^+(aq) + 2Cl^-(aq) →$
         $Mg^{2+}(aq) + 2Cl^-(aq) + H_2O(l)$

5 a) H^+ and OH^-;   b) H^+ and CO_3^{2-}

6 a) Add nickel(II) oxide to some dilute sulphuric acid until no more reacts. Filter off the excess nickel(II) oxide. Evaporate off some of the water. Allow to crystallise. Filter off the crystals of nickel(II) sulphate.
     b) $NiO(s) + H_2SO_4(aq) → NiSO_4(aq) + H_2O(l)$

7 Add a little indicator to some sodium hydroxide solution (or nitric acid). Add nitric acid (or sodium hydroxide) until the appropriate colour change takes place. Note the volumes used and repeat the mixing *without* the indicator. (This must be done, otherwise the indicator will colour the salt.) Evaporate off some of the water. Allow to crystallise. Filter off the crystals of sodium nitrate.

8 a) KCl(aq) or 2KCl(aq) for a balanced equation
     b) $CuCO_3(s) + Na_2SO_4(aq)$
     c) $AgCl(s) + LiNO_3(aq)$

9 $Cu^{2+}(aq) + CO_3^{2-}(aq) → Cu^{2+}CO_3^{2-}(s)$ **C**
    $Ag^+(aq) + Cl^-(aq) → Ag^+Cl^-(s)$

10   Making electricity

1 D

2 a) from zinc to copper
     b) The reading would be zero.
     c) The reading would decrease.

3 a) Displacement occurs when a metal is added to a solution containing ions of a metal lower in the ECS.
     b) Displacement only takes place in (iii)

> **4** $Mg(s) \rightarrow Mg^{2+}(aq) + 2e$ (oxidation)
> $e + Ag^+(aq) \rightarrow Ag(s)$ (reduction)
>
> **5** a) $Mg(s) \rightarrow Mg^{2+}(aq) + 2e$ (oxidation)
> $2e + 2H^+(aq) \rightarrow H_2(g)$ (reduction)
> b) $Mg(s) + 2H^+(aq) \rightarrow Mg^{2+}(aq) + H_2(g)$
>
> **6** a) reduction; b) reduction; c) none of these;
> d) reduction; e) redox; f) oxidation;
> g) oxidation
>
> **7** a) reduction
> b) from A to B
> c) (i) The blue colour of the solution intensifies
> as more $Cu^{2+}(aq)$ ions are formed;
> (ii) $Cu(s) \rightarrow Cu^{2+}(aq) + 2e$

11 Metals

1 a) F; b) A

2 low density and very strong

3

Coin	%Cu	%Ni	%Zn
20p	84	16	0
50p	75	25	0
£1	70	5.5	24.5

4 a) An alloy is a mixture of metals, or of metals and
non-metals, which have been melted together.
b)

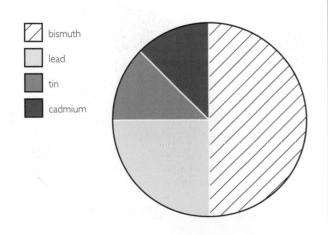

- bismuth
- lead
- tin
- cadmium

c) Wood's metal is used as a plug in the water
sprinkler heads that can be seen near the
ceilings of many shops and offices. In the event
of a fire the heat soon melts the plugs, letting
the water out.

5 a) sodium and potassium
b) green to violet
c) (i) lithium + water →
lithium hydroxide + hydrogen
(ii) $Li + H_2O \rightarrow LiOH + H_2$

> (iii) $2Li(s) + 2H_2O(l) \rightarrow$
> $2Li^+(aq) + 2OH^-(aq) + H_2(g)$

6 a) (i) magnesium + oxygen → magnesium oxide
(ii) $Mg + O_2 \rightarrow MgO$
(iii) $2Mg(s) + O_2(g) \rightarrow 2Mg^{2+}O^{2-}(s)$
b) (i) zinc + sulphuric acid →
zinc sulphate + hydrogen
(ii) $Zn + H_2SO_4 \rightarrow ZnSO_4 + H_2$
(iii) $Zn(s) + 2H^+(aq) + SO_4^{2-}(aq) \rightarrow$
$Zn^{2+}(aq) + SO_4^{2-}(aq) + H_2(g)$
c) (i) aluminium + hydrochloric acid →
aluminium chloride + hydrogen
(ii) $Al + HCl \rightarrow AlCl_3 + H_2$
(iii) $2Al(s) + 6H^+(aq) + 6Cl^-(aq) \rightarrow$
$2Al^{3+}(aq) + 6Cl^-(aq) + 3H_2(g)$

> **7** Aluminium is higher than zinc in the reactivity
> series/ECS and therefore forms more stable
> compounds than zinc. Aluminium bonds more
> strongly with oxygen than carbon does,
> whereas carbon bonds more strongly with
> oxygen than zinc does. As a result, when
> heated, carbon can take oxygen from zinc oxide
> but not from aluminium oxide.

8 a) $Sn^{2+}O^{2-}(s) + CO(g) \rightarrow Sn(s) + CO_2(g)$
$Cu^{2+}O^{2-}(s) + CO(g) \rightarrow Cu(s) + CO_2(g)$
b) Copper(II) oxide would be easier to convert
to the metal than tin(II) oxide because
copper is lower than tin in the reactivity
series/ECS. Copper therefore bonds less
strongly with oxygen than tin.
c) Both reactions are categorised as examples
of reduction because they involve a metal
compound being converted to a metal. In

both cases the important process taking place is gain of electrons by metal ions, e.g.
$$Cu^{2+} + 2e \rightarrow Cu$$

9   $PbO_2 + 2H_2 \rightarrow Pb + 2H_2O$

12   Corrosion

1   B and C

2   a) B;   b) B and E

3   a) a compound
    b) mercury or gold (both are below silver in the ECS)

4   a) ferroxyl indicator
    b) A blue colour/substance is formed.

5   a) The zinc coating prevents contact with air/oxygen and water.
    b) Since zinc is above iron in the ECS, electrons flow from zinc to iron, protecting the iron from corrosion.
    c) sacrificial protection

6   Aluminium is above iron in the ECS and since steel is mainly iron, electrons will flow from the aluminium to the iron. As a result of this the aluminium corrodes quite rapidly but the iron is protected.

7   a) A and C;   b) E

8   a) from the iron nail to the silver foil

    b) (i) $Fe \rightarrow Fe^{2+} + 2e$
       (ii) $4e + O_2 + 2H_2O \rightarrow 4OH^-$

9   a) Since iron is above copper in the ECS, electrons will flow from the iron, which is sacrificed, to the copper, which is protected. As a result the iron is expected to corrode quite rapidly.
    b) In order to eliminate corrosive effects there must be no electrical contact between the copper and the iron. There would have to be an insulator (non-conductor) between the two metals so that when bolted together electrons could not flow from one to the other.

10 a) iron nail B
    b) Electrons flow to nail B, which is therefore prevented from rusting, but away from nail A, which therefore rusts.
    c) The negative terminal of a car battery is attached to the steel body of the car.

13   Plastics

1   a) A;   b) E and F;   c) man-made

2

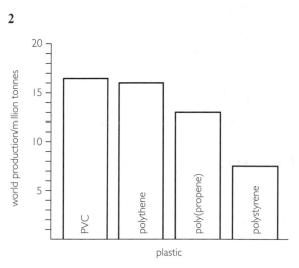

3   a) A thermoplastic polymer softens on heating and can be re-shaped.
    b) It can be used in many different ways – it has a wide variety of applications/uses.
    c)

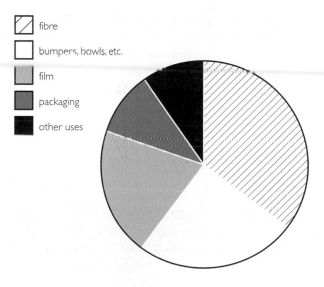

4 a) addition

b)

$$H - \underset{\underset{Cl}{|}}{\overset{\overset{H}{|}}{C}} - \underset{\underset{Cl}{|}}{\overset{\overset{H}{|}}{C}} - H \longrightarrow \underset{\underset{H}{\diagup}}{\overset{\overset{H}{\diagdown}}{C}} = \underset{\underset{Cl}{\diagdown}}{\overset{\overset{H}{\diagup}}{C}} \quad + \quad H - Cl$$

c) a plasticiser

d) It acts as a lubricant for the polymer chains.

5 Various answers are possible. For example, (i) most plastics are non-biodegradeable, so they survive for a long time; (ii) they are of low density, so they are very easily blown around, spreading far and wide.

6 a) poisonous; b) carbon monoxide;

> c) hydrogen chloride; d) hydrogen cyanide **C**

7 Thermoplastic because the methods used suggest that the plastics concerned must soften or melt during the processes mentioned.

8 It can stand contact with hot objects, such as pots and pans, without melting.

9 a) poly(tetrafluoroethene);

b) methyl-2-methylpropenoate

> **10** a) An addition polymer is produced in a process where many small monomers join to produce a polymer and nothing else. **C**
>
> b)
>
> $$... - \underset{\underset{F}{|}}{\overset{\overset{F}{|}}{C}} - \underset{\underset{F}{|}}{\overset{\overset{F}{|}}{C}} - \underset{\underset{F}{|}}{\overset{\overset{F}{|}}{C}} - \underset{\underset{F}{|}}{\overset{\overset{F}{|}}{C}} - \underset{\underset{F}{|}}{\overset{\overset{F}{|}}{C}} - \underset{\underset{F}{|}}{\overset{\overset{F}{|}}{C}} - ...$$
>
> c) The letters refer to certain parts in the name for the polymer, Poly(TetraFluoroEthene)

> **11** **C**
>
>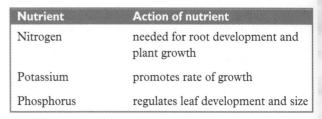
>
> (a) $- \underset{\underset{H}{|}}{\overset{\overset{Cl}{|}}{C}} - \underset{\underset{CH_3}{|}}{\overset{\overset{H}{|}}{C}} -$ (b) $\underset{\underset{H}{\diagup}}{\overset{\overset{Cl}{\diagdown}}{C}} = \underset{\underset{CH_3}{\diagdown}}{\overset{\overset{H}{\diagup}}{C}}$

14 Fertilisers

1 a) B and F; b) C and E; c) A; d) F; e) E; f) E

2 a) A nutrient is a substance which helps plants to grow.

b)

Nutrient	Action of nutrient
Nitrogen	needed for root development and plant growth
Potassium	promotes rate of growth
Phosphorus	regulates leaf development and size

> **3** a) sodium hydroxide **C**

b) Ammonia is less dense than air.

c) Ammonia is (very) soluble in water.

d) Ammonia has a sharp, unpleasant smell.

4 a) ammonia and oxygen

b) catalyst

c) The reaction between ammonia and oxygen is exothermic.

> d) $4NH_3 + 5O_2 \rightarrow 4NO + 6H_2O$ **C**

5 a) The energy from the lightning caused nitrogen and oxygen in the air to combine producing the acidic gas nitrogen dioxide. This dissolved in the rain water, increasing its acidity and thus lowering its pH.

b) The nitrogen dioxide dissolved producing nitric acid.

6 a) Fertilisers are substances which restore the essential elements for plant growth to the soil.

b) Increasing world population has led to a need for more efficient food production. Natural fertilisers alone cannot provide the necessary levels of crop production.

7 a) $KOH + HCl \rightarrow KCl + H_2O$

b) $\%K = \dfrac{\text{mass of K in formula}}{\text{formula mass}} \times 100$

$= \dfrac{39}{74.5} \times 100 = 52.3\%$

8 $Ca_3(PO_4)_2 + 3H_2SO_4 \rightarrow 3CaSO_4 + 2H_3PO_4$

9 a) $2NH_3 + H_3PO_4 \rightarrow (NH_4)_2HPO_4$

2 mol ⟷ 1 mol
34 g ⟷ 132 g
⟹ 34 kg ⟷ 132 kg
⟹ 1 kg ⟷ $\dfrac{132}{34}$ = 3.88 kg

b) $\%N = \dfrac{(2 \times 14)}{132} \times 100 = 21.2\%$

$\%P = \dfrac{31}{132} \times 100 = 23.5\%$

15 Carbohydrates

1 a) C and D; b) D and F; c) C and D; d) B

2 a) E; b) B;

c) D and F; d) B and C

3 a) Measure the freezing point ($0°C$) and boiling point ($100°C$).

b) On reaction with lime water, the lime water turned milky.

c) Carbon and hydrogen are present.

4 a) Glucose was present but not starch.

b) Glucose molecules are smaller than starch molecules. (Only glucose molecules are small enough to pass through the pores in the visking tubing.)

5 a) (i) Monomers are small molecules which can join together to form a very large molecule called a polymer.

(ii) A polymer is a very large molecule formed by the joining together of many small molecules called monomers.

(iii) Condensation polymerisation is a process in which many small molecules join to form a very large molecule, with water or another small molecule formed at the same time.

b) starch

6 a) (i) Hydrolysis is a reaction in which a large molecule is broken down into two or more smaller molecules by reaction with water.

(ii) An enzyme is a biological catalyst

(iii) The optimum temperature is the temperature at which the enzyme is most efficient/active.

b) pH

c) Glucose is the only product.
$C_{12}H_{22}O_{11} + H_2O \rightarrow 2C_6H_{12}O_6$
maltose   glucose

d) Spot X shows that some maltose remains in the solution and therefore the hydrolysis was incomplete.

part 2 Answers

16 Simple formulae for compounds I

1 a) Li_2O;   b) MgI_2;   c) H_2S;
   d) $AlCl_3$;   e) K_3N;   f) SnO_2;
   g) PBr_3;   h) BeS;   i) BN;
   j) Ca_3P_2;   k) NaF;   l) HF;
   m) CBr_4;   n) Mg_3N_2;   o) PH_3;
   p) SiO_2;   q) CaO;   r) B_2S_3;
   s) Al_2O_3;   t) NH_3;   u) $NaBr$;
   v) CaH_2

2 a) SCl;   b) $GeCl_4$;   c) CO;
   d) N_2O;   e) P_2O_3;   f) ClO_2

3 All apart from (b) disobey the valency rules.

4 a) Li_2SO_4;   b) $NaHCO_3$;   c) NH_4Br;
   d) K_3PO_4;   e) $RbNO_3$;   f) NH_4I;
   g) $MgCO_3$;   h) $KHSO_3$;   i) $LiOH$;
   j) NH_4NO_3;   k) $CaSO_4$;   l) $AlPO_4$;
   m) $NaHSO_4$;   n) KOH;   o) $NaMnO_4$;
   p) $MgSO_3$;   q) $BaCrO_4$;   r) $SrCO_3$;
   s) $K_2Cr_2O_7$;   t) Li_3PO_4;   u) Na_2SO_4;
   v) $KHCO_3$;   w) NH_4HSO_4;   x) NH_4NO_2

17 Simple formulae for compounds II

1 a) $CuCl$;   b) CuS;   c) Cu_2O;
   d) $FeCl_2$;   e) FeF_3;   f) MnO;
   g) MnO_2;   h) MnO_3;   i) Mn_2O_7;
   j) $CrCl_3$;   k) Cr_2O_3;   l) NiS;
   m) Ni_2O_3;   n) CrO_3;   o) V_2O_5;
   p) UF_6;   q) $SnCl_2$;   r) SnI_4;
   s) PbS;   t) $PbCl_4$

2 a) $Ca(NO_3)_2$;   b) $Ba(HCO_3)_2$;   c) $(NH_4)_2SO_4$;
   d) $Sr(HSO_3)_2$;   e) $(NH_4)_2CO_3$;   f) $(NH_4)_3PO_4$;
   g) $Al(OH)_3$;   h) $Mg(NO_3)_2$;   i) $Mg(HSO_4)_2$;
   j) $Ba(OH)_2$;   k) $(NH_4)_2Cr_2O_7$;
   l) $Ca(MnO_4)_2$;   m) $Mg_3(PO_4)_2$;   n) $(NH_4)_2SO_3$;
   o) $Ca(HCO_3)_2$;   p) $Al(NO_3)_3$

3 a) $CuCrO_4$;   b) $Pb(NO_3)_2$;   c) $Ba(MnO_4)_2$;
   d) $AgOH$;   e) $CuSO_4$;   f) $Sn(OH)_2$;
   g) $Cr_2(SO_4)_3$;   h) $Fe(NO_3)_3$;   i) $Mg(HSO_3)_2$;
   j) $AgNO_3$;   k) $Co(OH)_3$;   l) $FePO_4$;
   m) Ag_2CO_3;   n) $Hg(NO_3)_2$;   o) $SnCO_3$;
   p) $AuCl_3$

18 Chemical equations

1 a) $Mg + O_2 \rightarrow MgO$
   b) $CO + O_2 \rightarrow CO_2$
   c) $CH_4 + O_2 \rightarrow CO_2 + H_2O$
   d) $H_2S + O_2 \rightarrow SO_2 + H_2O$

2 a) $Na + Cl_2 \rightarrow NaCl$
   b) $Mg + F_2 \rightarrow MgF_2$
   c) $Al + I_2 \rightarrow AlI_3$
   d) $C + O_2 \rightarrow CO_2$
   e) $Li + H_2O \rightarrow LiOH + H_2$

3 a) $Li + Br_2 \rightarrow LiBr$
   b) $Na + O_2 \rightarrow Na_2O$
   c) $H_2 + Cl_2 \rightarrow HCl$
   d) $SiH_4 + O_2 \rightarrow SiO_2 + H_2O$
   e) $Ca + H_2O \rightarrow Ca(OH)_2 + H_2$

19 Balancing chemical equations

1 $2Li + Cl_2 \rightarrow 2LiCl$

2 $H_2 + I_2 \rightarrow 2HI$

3 $2Ca + O_2 \rightarrow 2CaO$

4 $N_2 + O_2 \rightarrow 2NO$

5 $Fe + 2HCl \rightarrow FeCl_2 + H_2$

6 $Mg + H_2SO_4 \rightarrow MgSO_4 + H_2$

7 $2Al + 6HCl \rightarrow 2AlCl_3 + 3H_2$

8 $2NaOH + H_2SO_4 \rightarrow Na_2SO_4 + 2H_2O$

9 $Ca(OH)_2 + 2HCl \rightarrow CaCl_2 + 2H_2O$

10 $Ba(OH)_2 + 2HNO_3 \rightarrow Ba(NO_3)_2 + 2H_2O$

11 $Sr(OH)_2 + H_2SO_4 \rightarrow SrSO_4 + 2H_2O$

12 $NH_3 + HCl \rightarrow NH_4Cl$

13 $2NH_3 + H_2SO_4 \rightarrow (NH_4)_2SO_4$

14 $3NH_3 + H_3PO_4 \rightarrow (NH_4)_3PO_4$

15 $4NH_3 + 3O_2 \rightarrow 2N_2 + 6H_2O$

16 $Fe_2O_3 + 3H_2 \rightarrow 2Fe + 3H_2O$

17 $PbO_2 + 2CO \rightarrow Pb + 2CO_2$

18 $2Al + Fe_2O_3 \rightarrow 2Fe + Al_2O_3$

19 $Fe_3O_4 + 2C \rightarrow 3Fe + 2CO_2$

20 $H_2O + CO \rightarrow H_2 + CO_2$

21 $4NH_3 + 5O_2 \rightarrow 4NO + 6H_2O$

22 $4FeS_2 + 11O_2 \rightarrow 2Fe_2O_3 + 8SO_2$

23 $MgCO_3 + 2HCl \rightarrow MgCl_2 + H_2O + CO_2$

24 $Na_2CO_3 + 2HNO_3 \rightarrow 2NaNO_3 + H_2O + CO_2$

25 $C_3H_8 + 5O_2 \rightarrow 3CO_2 + 4H_2O$

26 $C_2H_4 + 3O_2 \rightarrow 2CO_2 + 2H_2O$

27 $2C_4H_{10} + 13O_2 \rightarrow 8CO_2 + 10H_2O$

28 $C_5H_{12} + 8O_2 \rightarrow 5CO_2 + 6H_2O$

29 $2Ag_2CO_3 \rightarrow 4Ag + 2CO_2 + O_2$

30 $ZnCO_3 \rightarrow ZnO + CO_2$

31 $Mg + 2HNO_3 \rightarrow Mg(NO_3)_2 + H_2$

32 $(NH_4)_2Cr_2O_7 \rightarrow Cr_2O_3 + N_2 + 4H_2O$

33 $2Na + 2H_2O \rightarrow 2NaOH + H_2$

34 $Ca + 2H_2O \rightarrow Ca(OH)_2 + H_2$

35 $2Al + 3H_2SO_4 \rightarrow Al_2(SO_4)_3 + 3H_2$

36 $2KNO_3 \rightarrow 2KNO_2 + O_2$

37 $4HNO_3 \rightarrow 2H_2O + 4NO_2 + O_2$

38 $C_3H_6 + H_2O \rightarrow C_3H_8O$

39 $3LiOH + H_3PO_4 \rightarrow Li_3PO_4 + 3H_2O$

40 $2NaHCO_3 \rightarrow Na_2CO_3 + H_2O + CO_2$

41 $2Al + 3Br_2 \rightarrow 2AlBr_3$

42 $K_2CO_3 + H_2SO_4 \rightarrow K_2SO_4 + H_2O + CO_2$

43 $2Cu(NO_3)_2 \rightarrow 2CuO + 4NO_2 + O_2$

44 $2AgNO_3 \rightarrow 2Ag + 2NO_2 + O_2$

45 $6CO_2 + 6H_2O \rightarrow C_6H_{12}O_6 + 6O_2$

46 $C_6H_{12}O_6 \rightarrow 2C_2H_5OH + 2CO_2$

20 Ionic formulae for compounds   C

1 a) $(Li^+)_2O^{2-}$; b) $Mg^{2+}(I^-)_2$; c) $Al^{3+}(F^-)_3$;
d) $(K^+)_3N^{3-}$; e) $Ca^{2+}S^{2-}$; f) Na^+Br^-;
g) $(Ca^{2+})_3(P^{3-})_2$; h) $(Mg^{2+})_3(N^{3-})_2$;i) $Ca^{2+}O^{2-}$;
j) $(Al^{3+})_2(O^{2-})_3$; k) Rb^+Cl^-; l) $Sr^{2+}(Br^-)_2$

2 a) $Li^+NO_3^-$; b) $Na^+HCO_3^-$; c) $NH_4^+Cl^-$;
d) $Mg^{2+}CO_3^{2-}$; e) $Ca^{2+}SO_4^{2-}$; f) K^+OH^-;
g) $K^+MnO_4^-$; h) $Mg^{2+}SO_3^{2-}$; i) $Ba^{2+}CrO_4^{2-}$;

j) $NH_4^+NO_3^-$;　k) $K^+HSO_4^-$;　l) $Ca^{2+}Cr_2O_7^{2-}$

3　a) $(K^+)_3PO_4^{3-}$;　　b) $(Al^{3+})_2(SO_4^{2-})_3$;
　c) $(Li^+)_2CO_3^{2-}$;　　d) $Ca^{2+}(NO_3^-)_2$;
　e) $Ba^{2+}(HCO_3^-)_2$;　f) $(NH_4^+)_2SO_4^{2-}$;
　g) $(NH_4^+)_3PO_4^{3-}$;　h) $Al^{3+}(OH^-)_3$;
　i) $Mg^{2+}(HSO_4^-)_2$;　j) $(Ca^{2+})_3(PO_4^{3-})_2$;
　k) $(NH_4^+)_2SO_3^{2-}$;　l) $Ba^{2+}(MnO_4^-)_2$;
　m) $(Na^+)_2Cr_2O_7^{2-}$;　n) $Sr^{2+}(HSO_3^-)_2$

4　a) $(Ag^+)_2CrO_4^{2-}$;　　b) $Co^{2+}(NO_3^-)_2$;
　c) $(Cr^{3+})_2(SO_4^{2-})_3$;　d) $(NH_4^+)_2Cr_2O_7^{2-}$;
　e) $(Fe^{2+})_3(PO_4^{3-})_2$;　f) $Pb^{2+}(OH^-)_2$;
　g) $Mg^{2+}(HCO_3^-)_2$;　h) $Ba^{2+}SO_4^{2-}$;
　i) $Ni^{2+}(Cl^-)_2$;　　j) $Cu^{2+}CO_3^{2-}$;
　k) $Be^{2+}(F^-)_2$;　　l) $Hg^{2+}(NO_3^-)_2$;
　m) $Mn^{2+}(Br^-)_2$;　n) $Zn^{2+}O^{2-}$

21　Ionic and ion–electron equations

1　a) $CuO(s) + 2HCl(aq) \rightarrow CuCl_2(aq) + H_2O(l)$
　b) $Cu^{2+}O^{2-}(s) + 2H^+(g) + 2Cl^-(aq) \rightarrow$
　　　$Cu^{2+}(aq) + 2Cl^-(aq) + H_2O(l)$
　c) the oxide ion, O^{2-}, and the hydrogen ion, H^+

2　a) $Ba(OH)_2(aq) + H_2SO_4(aq) \rightarrow$
　　　$BaSO_4(s) + 2H_2O(l)$
　b) $Ba^{2+}(aq) + 2OH^-(aq) + 2H^+(aq) +$
　　　$SO_4^{2-}(aq) \rightarrow Ba^{2+}SO_4^{2-}(s) + 2H_2O(l)$
　c) the hydroxide ion, OH^-, and the hydrogen ion, H^+
　d) precipitation

3　a) $Fe(s) + 2HCl(aq) \rightarrow FeCl_2(aq) + H_2(g)$
　b) $Fe(s) + 2H^+(aq) + 2Cl^-(aq) \rightarrow$
　　　$Fe^{2+}(aq) + 2Cl^-(aq) + H_2(g)$
　c) $Fe(s) + 2H^+(aq) \rightarrow Fe^{2+}(aq) + H_2(g)$
　d) $Fe(s) \rightarrow Fe^{2+}(aq) + 2e$　　oxidation
　　　$2e + 2H^+(aq) \rightarrow H_2(g)$　　reduction

4　a) The solution turns from colourless to blue as colourless $Ag^+(aq)$ ions are replaced by blue $Cu^{2+}(aq)$ ions. The pink-brown copper becomes coated with silvery grey silver as the displaced silver forms as a layer on the copper.

b) $Cu(s) + 2Ag^+(aq) + 2NO_3^-(aq) \rightarrow$
　　　$Cu^{2+}(aq) + 2NO_3^-(aq) + 2Ag(s)$
　c) $Cu(s) + 2Ag^+(aq) \rightarrow Cu^{2+}(aq) + 2Ag(s)$
　d) $Cu(s) \rightarrow Cu^{2+}(aq) + 2e$　　oxidation
　　　$2e + 2Ag^+(aq) \rightarrow 2Ag(s)$　reduction

5　a) $Ni^{2+} + 2e \rightarrow Ni$　　reduction
　b) $2Br^- \rightarrow Br_2 + 2e$　　oxidation

22　Formula mass and the mole

1　a) 28;　b) 28;　c) 74;　d) 325;　e) 149;
　f) 342;　g) 58;　h) 98

2　Relationship used in each case is $m = n \times FM$
　a) 64 g;　b) $1.5 \times 40 = 60$ g;
　c) $2.25 \times 78 = 175.5$ g;　d) $4 \times 254 = 1016$ g
　$(= 1.016$ kg);　e) $0.25 \times 310 = 77.5$ g;
　f) $0.1 \times 340 = 34.0$ g;　g) $0.05 \times 148 = 7.4$ g;
　h) $500 \times 180 = 90\,000$ g $(= 90$ kg)

3　Relationship used in each case is $n = \dfrac{m}{FM}$
　a) $148/74 = 2$;　b) $50.5/101 = 0.5$;
　c) $294/84 = 3.5$;　d) $1000/100 = 10$;
　e) $1830/122 = 15$;　f) $0.195/78 = 0.0025$
　$(= 2.5 \times 10^{-3})$;　g) $100/58 = 1.72$;
　h) $500/96 = 5.21$

4　Mass of ammonium nitrate $=$
　$500 \times 1000 = 500\,000$ g
　Number of moles of $NH_4NO_3 =$
　$\dfrac{m}{FM} = 500\,000/80 = 6250$

5　Number of moles of aspirin $(C_9H_8O_4) =$
　$\dfrac{m}{FM} = 0.3/180 = 0.00167 \, (- 1.67 \times 10^{-3})$

6　Mass of water $= n \times FM = 11 \times 18 = 198$ g.
　1 cm^3 of water has a mass of 1 g. Thus, the volume of water $= 198 \, cm^3$

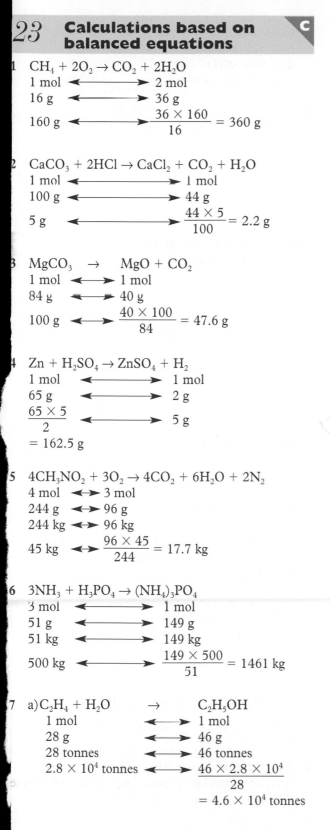

23 Calculations based on balanced equations C

1 $CH_4 + 2O_2 \rightarrow CO_2 + 2H_2O$
1 mol $\longleftrightarrow$ 2 mol
16 g $\longleftrightarrow$ 36 g
160 g $\longleftrightarrow$ $\dfrac{36 \times 160}{16} = 360$ g

2 $CaCO_3 + 2HCl \rightarrow CaCl_2 + CO_2 + H_2O$
1 mol $\longleftrightarrow$ 1 mol
100 g $\longleftrightarrow$ 44 g
5 g $\longleftrightarrow$ $\dfrac{44 \times 5}{100} = 2.2$ g

3 $MgCO_3 \rightarrow MgO + CO_2$
1 mol $\longleftrightarrow$ 1 mol
84 g $\longleftrightarrow$ 40 g
100 g $\longleftrightarrow$ $\dfrac{40 \times 100}{84} = 47.6$ g

4 $Zn + H_2SO_4 \rightarrow ZnSO_4 + H_2$
1 mol $\longleftrightarrow$ 1 mol
65 g $\longleftrightarrow$ 2 g
$\dfrac{65 \times 5}{2}$ $\longleftrightarrow$ 5 g
$= 162.5$ g

5 $4CH_3NO_2 + 3O_2 \rightarrow 4CO_2 + 6H_2O + 2N_2$
4 mol $\longleftrightarrow$ 3 mol
244 g $\longleftrightarrow$ 96 g
244 kg $\longleftrightarrow$ 96 kg
45 kg $\longleftrightarrow$ $\dfrac{96 \times 45}{244} = 17.7$ kg

6 $3NH_3 + H_3PO_4 \rightarrow (NH_4)_3PO_4$
3 mol $\longleftrightarrow$ 1 mol
51 g $\longleftrightarrow$ 149 g
51 kg $\longleftrightarrow$ 149 kg
500 kg $\longleftrightarrow$ $\dfrac{149 \times 500}{51} = 1461$ kg

7 a) $C_2H_4 + H_2O \rightarrow C_2H_5OH$
1 mol $\longleftrightarrow$ 1 mol
28 g $\longleftrightarrow$ 46 g
28 tonnes $\longleftrightarrow$ 46 tonnes
2.8×10^4 tonnes $\longleftrightarrow$ $\dfrac{46 \times 2.8 \times 10^4}{28}$
$= 4.6 \times 10^4$ tonnes

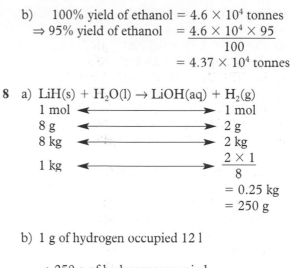

b) 100% yield of ethanol $= 4.6 \times 10^4$ tonnes
$\Rightarrow$ 95% yield of ethanol $= \dfrac{4.6 \times 10^4 \times 95}{100}$
$= 4.37 \times 10^4$ tonnes

8 a) $LiH(s) + H_2O(l) \rightarrow LiOH(aq) + H_2(g)$
1 mol $\longleftrightarrow$ 1 mol
8 g $\longleftrightarrow$ 2 g
8 kg $\longleftrightarrow$ 2 kg
1 kg $\longleftrightarrow$ $\dfrac{2 \times 1}{8}$
$= 0.25$ kg
$= 250$ g

b) 1 g of hydrogen occupied 12 l

$\Rightarrow$ 250 g of hydrogen occupied
$\dfrac{12 \times 250}{1} = 3000$ litres

24 Concentration and the mole C

1 Relationship used in each case is $C = \dfrac{n}{V}$

a) 3 mol/l; b) 0.5 mol/l; c) 5 mol/l;
d) 0.4 mol/l

2 Relationship used in each case is $n = C \times V$
a) 3 mol; b) 1 mol; c) 0.02625 mol;
d) 0.08 mol

3 Relationship used in each case is $V = \dfrac{n}{C}$

a) 5 litres; b) 30 litres; c) 0.3 litres; d) 2 litres

4 Relationships used in each case are
$n = \dfrac{m}{FM}$ and $C = \dfrac{n}{V}$

a) $n = 280/56 = 5$; $C = 5/2.5 = 2$ mol/l
b) $n = 6/120 = 0.05$; $C = 0.05/0.02 = 2.5$ mol/l
c) $n = 3.4/17 = 0.2$; $C = 0.2/0.05 = 4$ mol/l
d) $n = 100/116 = 0.862$;
$C = 0.862/0.8 = 1.08$ mol/l

5 Relationships used in each case are
$n = C \times V$ and $m = n \times FM$
a) $n = 0.1 \times 2.25 = 0.225$;
  $m = 0.225 \times 63 = 14.2$ g
b) $n = 18 \times 10 = 180$;
  $m = 180 \times 98 = 17\,640$ g $(= 17.64$ kg$)$
c) $n = 0.2 \times 0.65 = 0.13$;
  $m = 0.13 \times 261 = 33.9$ g
d) $n = 4.5 \times 0.2 = 0.9$; $m = 0.9 \times 40 = 36$ g

6 Relationships used in each case are
$$n = \frac{m}{FM} \text{ and } V = \frac{n}{C}$$

a) $n = 568/142 = 4$; $V = 4/2 = 2$ litres
b) $n = 3.7/74 = 0.05$; $V = 0.05/0.02 = 2.5$ litres
c) $n = 200/84 = 2.38$; $V = 2.38/0.6 = 3.97$ litres
d) $n = 1200/180 = 6.67$;
  $V = 6.67/1.4 = 4.76$ litres

25 Calculations based on titration results

1 a) $n_{NaOH} = C \times V = 0.2 \times 0.02 = 0.004$
  b) From the equation 1 mol HNO_3 reacts with 1 mol NaOH. Thus 0.004 mol HNO_3 reacts with 0.004 mol NaOH.

  c) $C_{HNO_3} = \dfrac{n}{V} = 0.004/0.01 = 0.4$ mol/l

  or
  $C_A = \dfrac{C_B \times V_B \times a}{V_A \times b} = \dfrac{0.2 \times 20 \times 1}{10 \times 1} = 0.4$ mol/l

2 a) From the equation 1 mol H_3PO_4 reacts with 3 mol KOH.
  b) $n_{H_3PO_4} = C \times V = 0.1 \times 0.04 = 0.004$
  c) Since 1 mol H_3PO_4 reacts with 3 mol KOH, 0.004 mol H_3PO_4 reacts with 0.012 mol KOH.

  d) $C_{KOH} = \dfrac{n}{V} = \dfrac{0.012}{0.01} = 1.2$ mol/l

  or
  $C_B = \dfrac{C_A \times V_A \times b}{V_B \times a} = \dfrac{0.1 \times 40 \times 3}{10 \times 1} = 1.2$ mol/l

3 $n_{NH_3} = C \times V = 0.5 \times 0.016 = 0.008$
From the equation 1 mol H_2SO_4 reacts with 2 mol NH_3. Thus 0.004 mol H_2SO_4 reacts with 0.008 mol NH_3.
$$C_{H_2SO_4} = \frac{n}{V} = \frac{0.004}{0.025} = 0.16 \text{ mol/l}$$
$$\text{or } C_A = \frac{C_B \times V_B \times a}{V_A \times b} = \frac{0.5 \times 16 \times 1}{25 \times 2} = 0.16 \text{ mol/l}$$

4 $n_{Ba(OH)_2} = C \times V = 0.2 \times 0.025 = 0.005$
From the equation 2 mol HNO_3 reacts with 1 mol $Ba(OH)_2$. Thus 0.01 mol HNO_3 reacts with 0.005 mol $Ba(OH)_2$.
$$V_{HNO_3} = \frac{n}{C} = \frac{0.01}{0.25} = 0.04 \text{ l} = 40 \text{ cm}^3$$
$$\text{or } V_A = \frac{C_B \times V_B \times a}{C_A \times b} = \frac{0.2 \times 25 \times 2}{0.25 \times 1} = 40 \text{ cm}^3$$

5 $n_{Ca(OH)_2} = C \times V = 0.05 \times 0.05 = 0.0025$
From the equation 1 mol H_2SO_4 reacts with 1 mol $Ca(OH)_2$. Thus 0.0025 mol H_2SO_4 reacts with 0.0025 mol $Ca(OH)_2$.
$$V_{H_2SO_4} = \frac{n}{C} = \frac{0.0025}{0.2} = 0.0125 \text{ l} = 12.5 \text{ cm}^3$$
$$\text{or } V_A = \frac{C_B \times V_B \times a}{C_A \times b} = \frac{0.05 \times 50 \times 1}{0.2 \times 1} = 12.5 \text{ cm}^3$$

6 $n_{HCl} = C \times V = 0.1 \times 0.025 = 0.0025$
From the equation 1 mol NH_3 reacts with 1 mol HCl. Thus 0.0025 mol NH_3 reacts with 0.0025 mol HCl.
$$C_{NH_3} = \frac{n}{V} = \frac{0.0025}{0.02} = 0.125 \text{ mol/l} \text{ (this is the diluted solution)}$$
Concentration of original ammonia solution $= 0.125 \times 100$ mol/l $= 12.5$ mol/l

26 Percentage composition by mass

1 a) %C $= 12/16 \times 100 = 75$
  b) %Ca $= 40/100 \times 100 = 40$
  c) %O $= 16/18 \times 100 = 88.9$
  d) %N $= 14/17 \times 100 = 82.4$
  e) %S $= 32/64 \times 100 = 50$
  f) %Mg $= 72/100 \times 100 = 72$
  g) %K $= 78/174 \times 100 = 44.8$
  h) %N $= 42/149 \times 100 = 28.2$
  i) %C $= 72/180 \times 100 = 40$
  j) %O $= 96/164 \times 100 = 58.3$

k) %H = 8/96 × 100 = 8.33
l) %P = 62/262 × 100 = 23.7

2   a) %C = 12/28 × 100 = 42.9;
        %O = 100 − 42.9 = 57.1
    b) %H = 1/36.5 × 100 = 2.74;
        %Cl = 100 − 2.74 = 97.26
    c) %Mg = 24/62 × 100 = 38.7;
        %F = 100 − 38.7 = 61.3
    d) %Al = 54/102 × 100 = 52.9;
        %O = 100 − 52.9 = 47.1
    e) %Na = 46/62 × 100 = 75.2;
        %O = 100 − 75.2 = 24.8
    f) %Li = 7/69 × 100 = 10.1;
        %N = 14/69 × 100 = 20.3;
        %O = 100 − 10.1 − 20.3 = 69.7
    g) %N = 14/53.5 × 100 = 26.2;
        %H = 4/53.5 × 100 = 7.5;
        %Cl = 100 − 26.2 − 7.5 = 66.3
    h) %Ca = 40/136 × 100 = 29.4;
        %S = 32/136 × 100 = 23.5;
        %O = 100 − 29.4 − 23.5 = 47.1
    i) %N = 28/132 × 100 = 21.2;
        %H = 8/132 × 100 = 6.1;
        %S = 32/132 × 100 = 24.2;
        %O = 100 − 21.2 − 6.1 − 24.2 = 48.5
    j) %Mg = 24/146 × 100 = 16.4;
        %H = 2/146 × 100 = 1.4;
        %C = 24/146 × 100 = 16.4;
        %O = 100 − 16.4 − 1.4 − 16.4 = 65.8
    k) %C = 144/342 × 100 = 42.1;
        %H = 22/342 × 100 = 6.4;
        %O = 100 − 42.1 − 6.4 = 51.5
    l) %Ca = 40/234 × 100 = 17.1;
        %H = 4/234 × 100 = 1.7;
        %P = 62/234 × 100 = 26.5;
        %O = 100 − 17.1 − 1.7 − 26.5 = 54.7

4   CaH_2 (mass of hydrogen
    present = 4.62 − 4.40 = 0.22 g)

5   $FeCl_2$ (mass of chlorine
    present = 9.07 − 4.00 = 5.07 g)

6   NiO (mass of oxygen
    present = 3.75 − 2.95 = 0.8 g)

7   a) CH_2 (% by mass of
        hydrogen − 100 − 85.71 = 14.29%)
    b) Molecular formula must be C_nH_{2n}, where n is a
        whole number. Formula mass of
        $C_nH_{2n} = (12 × n) + (2 × n) = 70$,
        i.e. $14n = 70$ therefore $n = 5$. Thus the
        molecular formula is C_5H_{10}.

8   a) BH_3
    b) Molecular formula must be B_nH_{3n}, where n is a
        whole number. Formula mass of
        $B_nH_{3n} = (11 × n) + (3 × n) = 28$,
        i.e. $14n = 28$ therefore $n = 2$. Thus the
        molecular formula is B_2H_6.

28 Types of chemical formulae

1   a) $C_2O_4H_2$;   b) CO_2H

2   a) $C_3H_8O_3$;   b) CH_3O;   c) CH_2OHCH_2OH

3

(or similar)

4   a) C_3H_6;   b) C_3H_7;
    c) $CH_3CH_2CH_2CH_2CH_2CH_2CH_2CH_3$;
    d)

27 Empirical formulae

1   a) CH_4;   b) CH_3;   c) CuF_2;   d) $CaBr_2$;
    e) P_2O_3;   f) HgI_2

2   a) CO;   b) SO_3;   c) $NiCl_2$;   d) Al_2S_3;   e) CuS;
    f) NCl_3

3   PbI_2 (mass of iodine
    present = 10.1 − 4.49 = 5.51 g)

H   H   H   H
| | | |
H − C − C − C − C − H
| | | |
H   H   H   H

5

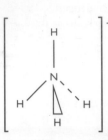

29 Types of chemical reaction

1 a) E; b) D; c) B; d) A; e) C

2 a) polymerisation; b) combustion;
   c) respiration *or* combustion; d) neutralisation;
   e) cracking; f) fermentation; g) precipitation;
   h) addition; i) photosynthesis;
   j) decomposition

3 a) C; b) F; c) A; d) B; e) D

4 a) condensation polymerisation;
   b) condensation; c) decomposition;
   d) reduction; e) neutralisation;
   f) redox *or* neutralisation *or* displacement;
   g) neutralisation; h) condensation;
   i) neutralisation; j) cracking

30 Identification tests

1 a) E; b) C; c) D; d) B

2 a) the carbohydrate is not starch; b) sucrose

3 a) red; b) orange-red; c) green; d) blue-green

4 Measure the boiling point (100°C) and freezing point (0°C).

5 a) ammonia
   b) Add dilute hydrochloric acid (or similar acid) to the solid. A gas is given off (carbon dioxide).

6 A blue colour appears around the iron nail, formed as a result of reaction between Fe^{2+}(aq) ions and ferroxyl indicator. A pink colour appears around the copper nail, formed as a result of reaction between OH^-(aq) ions and ferroxyl indicator.